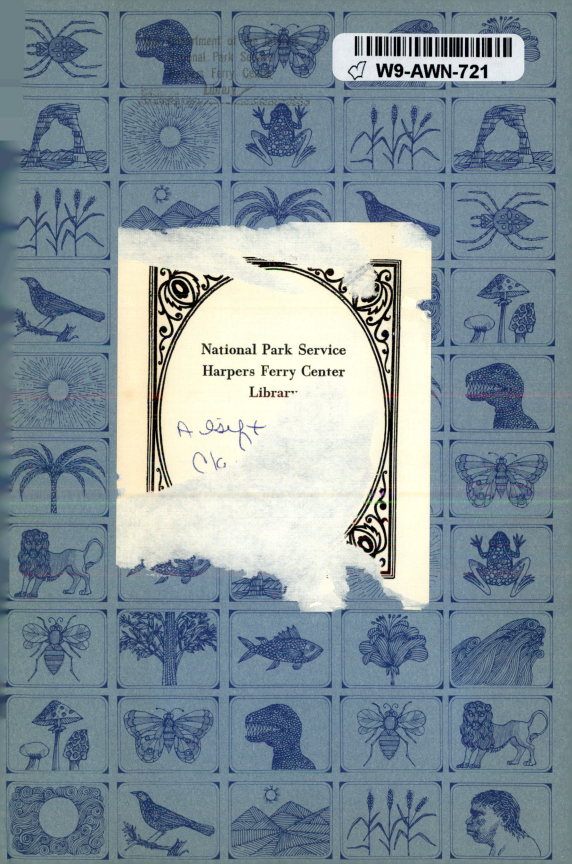

Other books by Hal Borland

Rocky Mountain Tipi Tales
Valor (JUVENILE)
Wapiti Pete (JUVENILE)
America Is Americans (POETRY)
An American Year
High, Wide and Lonesome
This Hill, This Valley
The Amulet

The Enduring Pattern

by Hal Borland

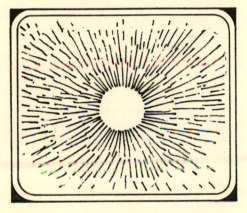

with drawings by Milton Glaser

SIMON AND SCHUSTER   NEW YORK, 1959

LIBRARY OF CONGRESS CATALOG CARD NUMBER: 59–13130
MANUFACTURED IN THE UNITED STATES OF AMERICA
BY KINGSPORT PRESS, INC., KINGSPORT, TENN.

To Barbara,
who shares the love, the laughter and the dreams

Contents

Foreword

THERE IS *a fundamental need in man to know three things: who he is, where he lives, and what time it is. With satisfying answers to those three questions, most of us could live in relative peace with the world and ourselves.*

Whether this need is peculiar to mankind I do not know; but I suspect that the intelligence, the emotion and the worries that are inherent in most of us make this need more urgent in the human being than in any other species of life. Perhaps when man advanced beyond that stage of life dominated by instinct and approached what we call reason he inherited this need as a part of the price.

I can answer those three questions, after a fashion, quite easily. I am a man, a member of the human race. I live in a par-

ticular valley on this planet, Earth. The time is the twentieth century.

But these easy answers are all superficial. Other questions come crowding after them. What is man? Where did he come from? What is his relationship to all the other forms of life around him? What is the earth, where did it come from, and how did it become the earth we know? And as for time, when I call this the twentieth century I am dating only one era of one phase of human life. How old is life? Where do I stand on the time scale of life? How long was yesterday, how long will today be, and what are the prospects for tomorrow? How long is the big time span, and what time is it now by that clock?

Men have been trying to find the answers for a long time, and other men have repeatedly challenged the answers because our store of knowledge is constantly changing. And every fact, every theory, must be approached skeptically because man provides all the evidence, appraises it, and makes the final judgment. The viewpoint is inevitably man's viewpoint because we have no other articulate witnesses. And man long ago demonstrated that neither his facts nor his judgments were infallible.

There were times when religion, then philosophy, seemed to provide ultimate answers. Then science came along and promised to rationalize everything, take all questions out of the realm of faith and answer them with facts. But science itself comes eventually to age-old ultimates, where factual explanation no longer suffices. Science reaches into the unknown with hypotheses, using a new language but reaching toward the same goals that religion and philosophy sought—a source, a beginning, an ultimate reason. When our physicists, who deal with matter and its laws of action, not long ago announced the theory of antimatter and antigravity, the religious philosophers must have recalled that they have long dealt with such antitheses—good and evil, God and the devil, creation and chaos. Possibly many scientists saw that a circle was closing too, for there are few

4

atheists among the foremost scientists. Albert Einstein once said, "That deeply emotional conviction of a superior reasoning power, which is revealed in the incomprehensible universe, forms my idea of God."

There is no alternative to belief in life. Man participates in it, partakes of it. He has, since the beginning, wanted to know more about it and, hence, more about himself. That, in one sense, is the ultimate search to which man is committed. That is the origin of those three questions: Who am I? Where am I? What time is it?

Life persists, and so does its ultimate source, call it what you will. Man is a unique form of that life, but not alien to it. He happens to live in the midst of life on this earth, this particular small unit of a universe about which he actually has only a smattering of knowledge. The chances are, barring inconceivably thorough self-destruction, that man will continue to live here a long time. Astrophysicists now say that the earth probably will be habitable for our own kind of life for another five billion years. Since man as a species appears by present estimate to be no more than one million years old, perhaps even less, the possibilities are stupendous.

Man has now begun to explore outer space, as we call it. But even in terms of our own solar system's dimensions, our rockets have thus far traveled only a little way. A rocket to the moon travels only about ten times the distance around the earth. And when I go out of doors at night, here in this valley where the glaciers plowed less than 25,000 years ago, I look up at the stars and think how many light-years they are away from where I stand, from where any human being stands. Even Mars, figuratively our neighbor just down the road, is 600 million miles away. Beyond Mars is Jupiter, more than a billion miles away. And beyond Jupiter, fading in the remote, incomprehensible distance, are four other known planets in our relatively minor solar system.

Despite the reach of our massive, far-seeing telescopes, which bring millions of stars and thousands of galaxies somewhat like our own into sight, the earth—and even our own planetary system—is a lonely place. And despite the vast libraries of our accumulated knowledge we know little about it. When I stand and look at the stars and feel a proper pride in human curiosity about the universe, I pause after a moment and realize that man still lives right here on earth, the earth of his own origins, and will continue to live here tomorrow and many more tomorrows. Here, not in outer space, man must find his answers if he is ever to find them.

And I must find them here in my own valley, at the foot of my own mountain. This is by no means all of the earth, nor even any considerable part of it; but it is of the earth, and in many ways it is typical. It has been here since there was enduring land above the waters of the earth, and life has been here since there was life anywhere upon the earth's land. If I cannot know something of myself and my place and time right here, I cannot know it anywhere.

So here is the earth, and here is life, and here am I, privileged for a little time to search for understanding. Religion helps, and philosophy helps, and science helps. But faith alone is not enough, reason is not enough by itself, and facts no matter how well organized are not enough. There must be some synthesis, some comprehension of faith and reason and fact all together.

What I have set down in the following pages is no more than one man's report of his search for the answers to those three basic questions. Whatever meaning emerges must come as much from the questions as from any possible answers. If there is meaning for anyone else, it is because we are searching together and because we have a common need to belong somewhere in the knowable universe.

We do belong, of course. We are the survivors, all of us, not

6

*of a man-made holocaust but of infinitely more powerful and
enduring forces, the surge of life, the rhythm of change, and the
infinity of time.*

H. B.

Weatogue
Salisbury, Connecticut
1959

A Place to Live

Time

Epochs, Eons and the Age of Mountains

Estimates of the age of the earth are largely guesswork, but most informed guessers say our particular planet came into being about three billion years ago, perhaps as much as five billion. How it came into being is a matter for theorists, but it is believed to have been whirling around the sun for one and a half billion years or more before any kind of life appeared upon it. How and whence that life came are also a matter of theory and speculation. Those who try to pin down its source, I have noticed, sometimes end up in myth or fable, sometimes rely on omnipotence, and sometimes honestly say, "We do not know—yet."

The first life, according to good evidence now available, appeared on earth about one and a half billion years ago. As far as we know, that life consisted of very small one-celled entities—

they may have been neither plant nor animal, but as yet undetermined in form. At first those bits of life lived in the warm waters of the earth, which presumably at that time were not saline as are the oceans of today.

From that earliest form of life evolved, more or less in succession, seaweed, sponges, small worms, shellfish, primitive fish with backbones, and the early amphibians and insects. From the amphibians came the first reptiles, and after them came the giants of their tribe, dinosaurs and their kind. The lizards persisted for about 150 million years. By the end of their age, birds and early mammals had appeared, forerunners of most of the animals we know today. Finally, perhaps a million years ago, the earliest form of man appeared.

Not only is the earth's age a matter of analytical guesswork, based on the best information available at the time the estimates are made, but so are the approximate dates of the geological and biological eras, periods and epochs. For a long time, for example, man firmly believed that the earth's age could be stated in terms of thousands, not millions and billions of years. Until recently the geologists and geophysicists based their estimates on sedimentation and erosion rates as revealed in the earth's rocks and the probable rate of salting in the oceans from leaching of the land. Recently the atomic physicists have provided a check on these estimates in the radioactive-component tests, which indicate how long the elements in the rocks have been radioactively "decaying." The radioactivity tests have already revised some of the geologic dates. For example, the last ice age was supposed to have ended about 25,000 years ago, according to geological evidence; but the radioactivity tests appear to make the date 11,000 years ago instead.

Few authorities have ever insisted that the geological dates generally accepted were absolute, but there has been general agreement that they were relatively correct. That is to say that the eras, periods and epochs did occur in the same order and in the same approximate relationships as those indicated in the dates suggested. It is that order and those relationships that are important, and there seems little doubt that the terms used, even in any revision of the actual dates, will still remain in the millions and even the billions of years. And it is in those terms that any broad view of the time span and the whole picture of life must be considered. It is the relative picture that is important, not the actual number of millions or hundreds of thousands of years that eventually may be accepted as absolute dates.

I have difficulty comprehending these enormous time spans. My life is bounded by hours, days, weeks, months, and a million or a billion years have little meaning. But I can begin to grasp the relative time spans if I compress them into terms of my daily experience.

Suppose we say, arbitrarily, that the world is forty-eight hours old, that it is now noon and that the earth was created at high noon day before yesterday. On that basis, the first form of life did not appear until noon yesterday. It was 9 o'clock last night before the first primitive sponges appeared. The first fish with a backbone, the earliest vertebrate, did not evolve until 4 o'clock this morning. It was 8:30 this morning, only three and a half hours ago, when the earliest form of plant life began to grow on land. At 9 o'clock the first amphibians appeared, and by 9:15 insects were here and growing swiftly in numbers. At 10 o'clock the dinosaurs and other giant lizards were present and thriving; they were still dominant when the first mammals appeared at 10:30, and they persisted until almost 11 o'clock. Then the mammals we know today began to dominate the scene. And finally, less than one minute ago, at a few seconds after 11:59, man came into being and began to develop.

When I first broke down the big time spans in this way I was suspicious of my own figures. But geologists and paleontologists are broadly agreed on the basic dates, and my figures are in agreement with their timetables. The Quaternary and Terti-

13

ary periods of geologic time, the past sixty-odd million years, represent less than 2 per cent of the total life span of the earth. In my compressed example they are represented by about 58 minutes—less than one hour.

So, whether we deal in incomprehensible billions of years or figuratively compress those years into a matter of hours, man is a newcomer on this earth. In a sense, he is still a stranger here, trying to fit himself into his environment and learning to live with his own kind and all the other forms of life around him. His tenure here is unpredictable, and even while he is here his life depends on a thousand variable conditions which are really beyond his own control. This should leave little room for human arrogance.

Each Spring when I watch the renewal of life after the time of Winter rest I realize once more that life as we know it and participate in it is a consequence of many balances and compromises. The Spring we see is evidence of the effect of those conditions, but the basic facts of the season we call Spring are few and simple. Spring comes when there is a rise of a few degrees in the average temperature from one week to the next, when there are a few more minutes of daylight from day to day, and when the angle of the sunlight changes a fraction of a degree. These things happen as a result of certain predictable movements in the planetary system to which the earth belongs. They are a part of a cosmic rhythm that apparently governs every planetary system we have ever discovered in the remoteness of space. Reviving life, as we see it in the form of opening buds, growing stems, nesting birds, birthing animals and blossoming flowers, depends on these essentially minor but inflexible changes, which are so slight that we would be unaware of them, certainly unaware of the day-to-day change, if there were not a response in all the forms of life around us.

Man has nothing to do with these conditions. They were here and they governed life long before man appeared, and they undoubtedly will be here for a long time to come. The best that man can do is chart Spring astronomically, then co-operate with it when it comes. Of all the machines ingenious man has invented, not one can create a living flower. We can incubate birds, we can artificially inseminate cows and even our own women, we can force buds into bloom, we can grow lettuce and tomatoes in a greenhouse; but in every instance we must start with a natural germ of life, and we must abide by basic rules that have governed natural reproduction and growth since far back in the unknown past. Man cannot change the rules.

I live in a rural valley, and when Spring comes my farmer neighbors do their Spring plowing and planting. They have good, modern farm equipment, as good as money can buy. But when they go out to plow they merely stir the soil, break it up, aerate it and mix in a few chemical concentrates and the winter manure from the cow barns. At a proper time they plant chosen germs of life, seed corn, and oats, and clover. From that moment on they must depend on the soil, the sun, the rain, the more or less varying conditions of nature. They cultivate their corn to discourage the weeds, but beyond that there is little they can do except hope that their degree of co-operation with the rules of growth has been sufficient and wisely planned and executed. If that is true, they will have a harvest.

This is a basic truth which every farmer knows. It is a truth with which anyone close to the land grows up and lives all his life. It becomes a part of him; it governs his way of thinking. Spring follows Winter, Summer follows Spring. And after Summer comes Fall, then another Winter, another Spring. The round of the seasons, the round of the years. There is planting, there is consequent growth, and there is rewarding harvest. There is cause, and there is inevitable effect.

I think of Spring as a beginning only because the human mind and habit tend that way. Human creatures like to count. They like matters to be neatly parceled, with beginnings and endings. That is one reason we devised a calendar and a clock, and one reason we call sundown the end of a day and sunrise the beginning. But few matters have such neat beginnings and endings. There is a continuance, a progression or at least a continuity. Spring is a quickening, but it is no more a beginning than is high noon or mid-July. It is only another aspect of that which is continuous.

There are, to be sure, annual plants and seasonal insects as well as those which live on from year to year. But annual plants grow from seeds, and the insects come from some egg form. The seeds and the eggs are no more than capsulated life carried over from one generation to the next. Somewhere along the long path of evolution, those plants and those insects found it more advantageous to trust their precious germ of life to a dormant seed or an egg than to try to hoard it in a root or a body over the Winter. There are also such plants as the bristle-cone pines of California that have lived as growing trees for at least 4,600 years. And there are periodic locusts which live in the ground as grubs for fifteen years or more before they emerge to acquire wings, eat, mate, create a din, lay eggs and die, all within an adult life span of only a few weeks or so. They merely prove that Spring is but one point in the vastly larger rhythm of life and time.

Spring happens to be the obvious time, the season of spectacular change, of growth and flowering and hatching and birthing in a multitude of ways, since life is almost infinitely various. We see life burgeoning. We are made aware of life and sometimes we celebrate its existence. More often we merely celebrate our own existence and indulge our pride in being a superior form of life.

There is no doubt of man's superiority, from his own viewpoint. As far as we know, man is unique; but that judgment quite possibly is biased and based on incomplete knowledge. We do know that man is endowed with intelligence, understanding, ingenuity, imagination and the elements of compassion. These are important attributes. They have enabled man to survive and progress, to a degree, in this precarious environment which, over the ages, has rid itself of any number of creatures that seemed to be better fitted, physically, than man is to survive.

Many animals of the past were bigger, stronger, better armed or armored than relatively puny man. A good many animals today are better equipped physically for survival. The insects long ago achieved something close to perfection; ants, bees and dragonflies have been on earth in substantially the same form we know today for at least sixty million years, sixty times as long as man has been here. Some of the shellfish have been here a billion years. Some of the single-celled plants and animals have been here even longer than that.

But man, ill equipped as he is, having no claws, no fangs, no wings, no thick fur, no feathers, no scales, unable to hibernate, only nominally prolific—man has persisted and become dominant.

Why?

Because man had more brain capacity than those creatures who preceded him, and he had the urge to use that power. Man invented speech, a means of shaping ideas and communicating them. When he began to talk and think about matters beyond his own rather limited self he began to outrank all other forms of life around him. Thus man became a creature with a dual nature—he was an animal who still needed food and shelter, but he was also a rational, thinking, emotional being with the urge to know and understand the conditions and limitations of the life of which he was a part. He began to examine the world around him and reach beyond the range of instinct into the realm of reason and imagination. Those two capacities, reason and imagination, apparently have made man what he is today.

Biologically, I am an animal. I need food and water to sustain me and I can tolerate only a relatively narrow range of temperature and humidity. Because I am a weakling among animals, I need clothing and shelter against the extremes of heat and cold. I am capable of procreation. I am a mobile creature; I can move about from place to place. My life span is relatively limited, since I am subject to disease and injury and because I, like all living creatures, am going to wear out as an organism.

I am omnivorous, eating either plants or animals. But, like all other animals, I can subsist only on other living things or their products. That proves that I am an animal, not a plant, because only plants can live on inorganic, nonliving substances. Yet my blood, in terms of chemistry, contains a substance not greatly different from the chlorophyll in green leaves, the substance which enables plants to create food from air, moisture and sunlight. This substance, hemoglobin, enables me to take oxygen from the air which is essential to my life processes. And the substance of my flesh and bones and vital organs is, chemically, almost pure mineral.

But somewhere in that complex of material of which I am composed is the element of life, which governed my life and my growth from the time I first appeared as a fertilized ovum only a quarter of a millimeter in diameter. That life force created me and it sustains me, as an animal creature.

Somewhere along the road of evolution from whatever ancient creature was the human ancestor, the node of nerves that enabled the body to perform its simple acts of living began to grow and change. Out of that elemental nerve center eventually evolved a brain, and the brain has reached its present degree of development only in man. That brain is the primary difference between me and other animals.

What happens in my brain is only dimly understood. Orders go out from there to the muscles and other elements of my body, apparently by rhythmic impulses along the network of nerves.

18

I do not understand this, although I am using that power in attempting to discuss it. We say that thought consists of ideas and their interrelation. But how explain an idea? The power of thought apparently is related to rhythmic impulses and, in one way or another, to all the senses.

When I reach that point I think how completely my life processes are dominated by rhythms. My breathing, my pulse, my unconscious processes of digestion, my hearing, my eyesight, my sense of touch, my speech and my thoughts—all are matters of rhythm.

Life is governed by the rhythms. The female animal has rhythmic periods of fertility. The sex act of fertilization is rhythmic. Birth is accomplished in rhythmic labor. And all the rhythmic processes I mentioned just above are essential to growth, maturity and the continuation of life. When they cease, a unit of life has come to its physical end.

Until man evolved, with his power of thought, imagination, speech and communication, and until he created the means of exchanging and accumulating knowledge and ideas, one generation to the next, life was primarily a matter of survival and change was largely limited to accident and evolution. Man has altered that somewhat, particularly with relation to his own kind and to those forms of life on which he is dependent or which immediately endanger him. But mostly man has changed himself as he advanced from the trees to the caves, from the caves to the river valleys, from the valleys onto the open plain, thence out across the whole of the land until every habitable part of the world came to know him.

Man has done some remarkable things, but he has never escaped his link with the basic rhythms. He never will. What he has accomplished has been within the framework of those natural laws, and his primary achievements have been in the study and use of those laws. And he still must live in the environment to which he was born—this planet, this earth. He

19

now talks of exploring other planets, but even his plans for that are limited by the conditions of the planetary system whose center is the sun, and they are in terms of the laws with which we have learned to live here on earth—such fundamental laws as those of gravity, light, sound, time, atomic motion. And all those plans are limited by that mysterious rhythmic capacity in us, that power of thought.

The disquieting element in all this is man's tendency to drift or stray from the basic elements of his own environment, the fundamental rhythms of life. As he evolves complexities of living which he calls civilization he loses perspective on himself and his cosmos. He sometimes thinks that he can ignore or repeal the most enduring fundamental of all, cause and effect. And he tends to minimize the importance of life itself—not his own life, perhaps, but that great stream of life of which he is only a part.

I am writing this in the Springtime, and I am tempted to say a foolish thing: that the one enduring reason for those obvious and rhythmic changes we know as the seasons of the year is to demonstrate the cycles of persistent and pervading life. The whole of life, in a sense, is concentrated into the year, the single round of the sun—birth, growth, maturity, and the pause between generations.

I know perfectly well that nature has no such purpose. Nature is an infinitely complex series of facts; it is not an object lesson, and it is not a ready-made sermon on conduct or morality. Any lessons to be learned from the world and the cosmos where we live are a result of man's own need for understanding. Yet the question persists: If I have the intelligence to seek, to wonder, to ask for reason and order, may there not be some power of reason and order beyond my knowing? Is man's intelligence unique, or is there some source, some vast and remote ultimate of reason, which man can approach and in which man, to a slight degree, participates?

Today I know that it is Spring, because the sun came up this morning just a bit north of east and it will be in the sky a few minutes longer today than it was yesterday. The vernal equinox occurred less than a week ago. Astronomically speaking, that was the beginning of Spring in this Northern Hemisphere where I live. If everything were ordered by man's precise calculations, I could tell you the exact minute when the first violet would bloom and when the blossoms on my apple trees would open. But our charts and calculations are nothing more than observed facts about the movement of the earth around the sun and the earth's inclination on its own axis. And Spring is something that happens here, not in the orbit of the earth. Here, in the soil beneath my feet, in the air around me, even in myself.

Spring is something that happens in the whole pulse of life, and I am fortunate to live where I am daily made aware of this. Certain movements of the earth are involved, but essentially Spring is such simple things as a slow warming of the soil, frost oozing away and streams full and springs bubbling. It is the migrant birds making the dawn loud and sweet again as they take up seasonal residence, preparing to build nests and lay eggs and hatch fledglings. It is you and I going out to the garden plot to investigate the state of the soil and look for the first crinkled red leaves of rhubarb, the fine green shoots of chives thrusting up from the withered tangle of last year's growth, and hoping that there will be no late frost to nip the daffodils already in bud.

The clock of all time may be in the stars, but the clock of the year, and especially of Spring and of all the life we know, is in the earth whence all that life sprang. It is in the radish seed and the onion bulb and the root of the dandelion. How it got there I do not know, but there it is, ticking away the days and hours. I see the proof every year, and I am sure that I shall see it each Spring as long as I live. It will be there long after I am gone.

It is Spring, and down the road the peepers, the tree frogs that hibernated in the muck of the bogland all Winter, are shrilling that they are alive and life is urgent. There they are, and here am I, and between us there is a large measure of understanding. We are sharers of life, the great inheritance. I like to think that I know more about it than they do, but that is perhaps debatable. I think, and I feel, to a degree. The peepers have few thoughts, if any, though they must have intense feelings. But we are kin, and we would do well never to forget that if we would have any understanding of life and of our own kind. For life is the common denominator among all of us, life and the conditions of its beginnings and its continuance.

The Land

This Earth and the Forces That Shaped It

YESTERDAY was one of those mild days of late March when what I hope was the last heavy snow of the Winter melted steadily under the strengthening sun. Water was everywhere, in big shallow ponds in the pasture, in hollows at the roadside, leaping in brooks that lapped at their banks, gently swelling the river which flows majestically down this valley. All afternoon there was the sound of flowing or trickling water on the mountainside back of the house.

In early afternoon I went out to the vegetable garden patch and found water from an overflowing pasture pond eating its way across the space where we hope to plant sweet corn and lima beans in a few more weeks. A brand-new brook was chewing out a channel in the rich, rootless garden soil. I had to get a spade and build a temporary diversion dam before the water gullied the whole garden.

Even as I was piling sod and pasture soil in the dam I knew that, in this small area of this relatively minor valley, I was watching fundamental forces. Here on this mild Spring day I was seeing, on a miniature scale, the way this whole continent was shaped to its present familiar outlines. I was watching water eat away a mountain and move fresh soil into a valley, watching a new brook try to form a bed. What was happening right here on my farm was a result of eons of earthquakes, volcanic eruptions, floods, droughts, ice ages and howling winds.

This place where I live is a small portion of the Housatonic Valley in the Berkshire Hills. The Berkshires once were high mountains, among the earlier upthrusts that eventually shaped this continent. There are rocks here that date back, I am told, to the Cambrian period, some 550 million years ago. Those Cambrian marbles contain fossils which the paleontologists identify as among the oldest on earth, fossils of primitive forms of shellfish that were here before any creatures developed backbones and long before there were any forms of plant life on the land.

These mountains are younger than the rocks, perhaps 150 or 200 million years old. When I try to look back down that corridor of time I begin to lose all sense of time and most of my perspective. I can almost envision a million years, which is ten thousand centuries. But when I get to the billions I am lost. A billion years is ten million centuries, and to me that is like trying to count the raindrops in a cloudburst. When a geologist tells me that the earth is three billion years old—or five billion, as some say—I am tempted to ask how he knows that his figure is correct to the nearest million. Then I make a mental calculation and I hold my tongue. An error of one million in three billion would be an error of three tenths of one per cent, the equivalent of one cent in thirty dollars.

But apparently the earth is between three and five billion years old, and it spent half or more of that time settling down into a relatively solid planet of rock and water. For another billion years it underwent convulsions before any massive land form emerged. And it was not until about 200 million years ago that the beginnings of the continents as we know them took shape. Another fifty million years or so and the basic mountains of northeastern America had risen. Then came the rough outlines of this continent. And about a million years ago, around the time when the first primitive forms of man evolved, the forces that shaped this land somewhat as we know it began to work on comparatively stable land masses. That was when what we call the recent ice ages began.

Most of the North American continent and much of Europe and northern Asia were shaped by the ice ages, when tremendous glaciers, some of them a mile thick, pushed down from the north and scarred and scoured the land. All of Canada and the northern half of the United States were covered by the ice. Every mountain in the way, including the Sierra Nevada, the Rockies and the Appalachians and Adirondacks, was gouged and whittled away, often to the core of ancient rock. But besides the gouging and scarring, which scooped out thousands of lakes ranging in size from Lake Superior down to the pond which lies just over the mountain behind my house, there was the complex effect of alternate freezing and thawing, advance and retreat, of the ice sheet. Vast quantities of sand, gravel, broken rocks and other debris were dumped over the land, and oceans of water flowed away, the melt from the ice. There was a whole series of advances and retreats by the ice, so this erosion by flood and flowing water, with its consequent deposit, was repeated time and again.

What happened was the same thing that happened yesterday on my mountainside, in my pastures and in my garden, though instead of being a few trickles down one slope and a few overflows from one pasture pond across a small patch of garden soil, whole continents were involved. Lakes hundreds of miles across were formed. Tremendous rivers went roaring across the land, ripping their way to the oceans, stripping topsoil and baring the bedrock, forming vast deltas and alluvial flats. The major drainage systems of the United States, not to mention Europe and Asia, were formed. Our whole Midwest was a shallow sea, a northward extension of the Gulf of Mexico. My relatively placid Housatonic was probably an awesome torrent flowing several hundred feet over its present bed, and the whole of Connecticut was covered with glacial debris which the streams gullied deep and carried, as silt and gravel, and dumped in huge quantities just beyond their mouths. Some of that glacial debris, carried away by those torrential streams, helped form the huge sand-and-gravel bar that we now call Long Island.

Finally the glaciers retreated and did not return. The date of the retreat varied from place to place, but there had been repeated advances and retreats of the ice, and the ice ages had persisted for several hundred thousand years. When the ice finally went away we were rid, at last, of the final major force which greatly shaped the land. Then the lesser forces, wind, rain, frost and flowing water, went to work. They are still at work, constantly trying to level the hills and fill the valleys, but we are seldom aware of them unless a major river goes on a rampage, or a long drought and unremitting winds sweep the High Plains, or a tidal wave clears a shore line and builds a new series of offshore sand bars. Or until a heavy snow melts in the spring thaw and I find a new brook eating away my unprotected garden soil.

But I have seen all these forces at work right here in this microcosm, and from the minor examples I can see what they have been doing over the centuries and the eons to the land masses everywhere.

Fifty years or so ago a power company built a dam across the Housatonic half a mile below my house and in-

stalled a hydroelectric plant there. It was a dam of only moderate height, and it raised the river level only five or six feet,
certainly less than ten. But the river has only a slight fall in this
area, and that rise in the river level created a marshland of
considerable area over the old flood plain just upstream from
here. Old-timers still talk in hushed tones of the vast flocks of
wild fowl and of the big fish that used to live there. Then, just
twenty years ago, there was a flood. It washed out one wing of
the dam. Overnight the water level of the river dropped five or
six feet. The dam was never restored. Today that marsh is
gone. In its place is a broad, low, sandy meadow area with a
brook winding across it. Overnight, the whole character of this
part of the valley was changed. And when the river level
dropped, so did the water table. Shallow wells along the valley
went dry. The character of the vegetation changed. Even the
climate changed somewhat.

Change is still going on in the vanished swampland. The
brook that flows across the old marsh bed empties into the
Housatonic behind an island. That island originally was only a
sand bar, formed of silt carried down by the brook and emptied
at its mouth, but today it is an island a hundred yards long and
covered with trees. Until three years ago the brook flowed
around both ends of the island in channels four or five feet
deep. I often used those channels in my small fishing boat.

Then we were struck by the tail end of a hurricane and had
a consequent flood. Flood waters brought a cargo of uprooted
trees and brush down the brook and dumped them in the lower
channel back of the island. Sand and gravel also brought down
by the flood were dropped there and anchored the driftwood.
I could still get around the island in my boat, but the channel
was shallower and partially clogged. The next spring brought
normal high water and the usual freight of brush and other
trash. It lodged in the initial tangle and trapped more sand
and silt. Last year I could no longer get through that channel,

27

though my boat has only a six-inch draft. Now there is only a trickle through it, and this year's spring freshets probably will almost close it. In another year or two there will be no channel there. The island will have become a peninsula. And this has happened in only three years.

On up the Housatonic a few miles another brook flows into it, a meandering stream that crosses a broad, flat meadow. Years ago that stream was a leaping mountain brook plunging down a rocky valley fringed with birches and aspens. Then a family of beavers came there and built a dam. They created a small pond at the head of the valley, cut or drowned most of the trees, and moved on down the stream a little way. They and their offspring built another dam, and still another. It became a beaver valley with a whole series of dams which checked the flow of the brook. The dams began to silt up and grow over with water plants. Eventually the whole valley was a broad bog thick with moss and rotting vegetation. Then trappers came, took the beavers, and the dams rotted away. The brook ran free again, but now it was a slow, winding stream through a marshy flat overgrown with brush. A farmer came who wanted a new field. He cut the brush and the sun began to dry the swamp. The brook drained its excess water. In a few more years that valley was a broad, flat expanse of rich topsoil with a quiet brook flowing through it. Today it is a fertile field, a typical beaver valley created by the wash of a stream when a dam or other barrier persuades that stream to drop its load of silt.

Back of my house stands a high hill known on the old maps as Tom's Mountain. It is a part of a ridge that runs approximately north and south. When the glaciers came this way they rode that ridge and gouged out the valley where my house now stands, because the rock that was here was softer than the rock core of the ridge. Occasionally I climb to the top of Tom's Mountain to look at the marks of those glaciers. All that the ice left of the original mountain, up there at the summit, was its massive core of stubborn mica schist, now weathered and frost-split but still obdurate and still showing the scars and scratches of the passage of the ice perhaps 25,000 years ago.

On the other side of Tom's Mountain lies another valley, where the ice must have found an even softer streak of rock than it found on my side of the mountain. It gouged particularly deep, and when it retreated it left a lake there. After the lake had spilled its excess it settled down to something like its present form, fed by half a dozen small brooks and nobody knows how many springs.

Most of the small lakes and ponds in this area are shallow, but this one drops off sharply only a little way from shore and is sixty to a hundred feet deep, with a rock bottom. It is one of the deeper pittings on the local landscape left by the glaciers.

Just below this lake and connected with it by a neck is another pond like dozens of others hereabout. It is shallow and marshy and has a muddy bottom on top of a deep layer of sand, gravel and other sedimentary deposit on the bedrock. It is called the deep lake's twin, but they are totally unlike. The lower lake, the shallow one, probably was formed by beaver dams or other barriers in the original outlet from the deep lake. Both of them, in totally different ways, were formed by the ice age and its aftermath. Both are footprints of the glaciers.

On my side of Tom's Mountain are a number of rocky ledges. They have been exposed to the elements for thousands of years; because they are more or less sheer ledges they have little protection, almost no soil cover, few bushes and fewer trees. Lichens grow on them and here and there a clump of grass has found a foothold. But, as I say, they are almost constantly exposed to sun, wind, rain, snow, ice and trickling water.

Water is the major enemy of those ledges. It is slowly eating them away. What erosion is done by the trickling water, however, is of minor importance. The major destruction of those rocks comes from thin films of water that seep into every minute crack and, when the frosts come, turn to ice. Ice is nature's all-powerful pry-bar, her splitting wedge. Even the thinnest film of ice exerts enormous pressure. Each spring when I go up there I see fresh faces on those ledges and find fresh talus on the slopes beneath them. The slow teeth of time are eating away those rocks that defied the giant cutting edge of the glaciers. When I walk along the top of those ledges I must watch my footing, for there is always a freshly loosened rock or a whole section of ledge that may give way under my weight. Someday there will be no ledges left there. But not in my time, and probably not in the time of man.

I come down the mountain a little way from the ledges and I find a bog a few acres in extent. Within his own memory, a neighbor tells me, that bog was a hayfield. It then was drained by a brook that the farmer who lived here kept clear. Eventually he abandoned that hayfield, which was difficult to reach from the valley, and the brook became clogged, probably with leaves, roots and natural trash. Now the field is a bog and only a trickle of water flows in the old brook, and where hay once grew now stand white pines ten inches through and white birches and alder bushes. But that moist bogland serves me well, for it undoubtedly helps feed the big spring, a little farther down the mountainside, which provides the water for my house.

Within only thirty or forty years that little patch of ground well up the mountainside has changed several times. First it was a damp, wild natural meadow at the foot of the ledges, watered by a few seep springs. Then a farmer cleared it, gave it drainage, made it a hayfield. He kept down its natural growth of brush and trees. Then he abandoned it and nature took charge once more. It gradually became a shallow bog. Brush grew there, then short-lived trees, then the pines crept in. Today it is wild again, and its thick mat of roots and decaying vegetation forms a reservoir for water that feeds the springs on down the mountainside. And slowly the gradually crumbling

ledges above it encroach with their disintegrating rock, the unending tendency of the high places to fill the low ones. Already
the upper edges of that little bogland are studded with rocks as
big as a barrel, weathered debris from the ledges that the ice
pried loose and gravity rolled down the slope.

When I follow that trickle of a brook from the bog on down
the mountainside I can see, compressed into less than half a
mile, the whole story of how ice and water reduce rocks to
sand and spill a constant load of silt into the valleys.

From the bog the stream trickles for a little way among big
boulders, with virtually no sand or gravel in its bed. Then the
surrounding rocks are smaller and the stream bed is covered
with broken rock in chunks about the size of my two fists. I
come on downstream, the volume of water increases and its fall
becomes hurried, and the stream bed is lined with smooth
stones the size of one fist. This size diminishes each rod of the
way, to that of a baseball, of a golf ball, of a marble, and finally,
at the last bench before the valley, to coarse sand. Then the
brook spills out onto the last, gentle slope of the valleyland
pasture and its sand is finer than cornmeal. For centuries that
flowing water has been grinding away at those rocks, rubbing
and jostling one against another, gradually reducing them to
sand.

Last summer I had to dig a ditch here at the house, a ditch
five feet deep. The first foot down was through fine black topsoil, the kind of rich soil that is built up on any good farm by an
accumulation of humus and organic matter. Some small part of
it may have been deposited here by the river long ago, for my
house site and the pastures are on the old flood plain, as are
most valley lands. But beneath that layer of topsoil I came to
fine, tan-colored sand, fine as the finest sand in the brook I
followed down the mountain, and the same color. There was
three feet of that sand before I came to a coarser layer. It was
still sand, but the grains were twice or three times as large as

31

those of the sand just above it. There probably was three feet of that coarse sand, though I did not penetrate it with my ditch. Beneath it was still coarser material, and beneath that was gravel. I am sure of this for two reasons. First, that is the way such deposits are laid down by flowing water—the coarse layers, then the increasingly finer ones. And, second, I drove a well point, as we say, a few years ago. I went down twenty feet or so and could tell by the way the pipe penetrated the soil what type of material was there, almost foot by foot.

What I was doing when I drove that well point, and when I dug that ditch, was digging down into Tom's Mountain. I was penetrating not only this valley soil, but the mountain's history and the history of the valley. Every grain of that fine sand and a good deal of the topsoil originally was up there on the mountainside. Most of it was once the basic rock of the mountain's skeleton, the tough rock that defied the glaciers. It was ground up, bit by bit and century by century, by flowing water. And that same water carried it down here and dropped it where it lies now.

Somewhere down there beneath that topsoil and sand and gravel lies bedrock, the old rock that was scoured clean by the passage of the glaciers. It doesn't lie very deep, and it reveals itself in outcroppings all down the valley. When the highway people rebuilt the road through here a few years ago they had to blast bedrock ledges at a dozen places, and each blast jolted the house and made the water in the river quiver. Such explosions would be dampened, certainly not transmitted this far, if there were a deep layer of soil or if the exposed rocks were only random patches rather than outcroppings of the foundation stone for the whole area.

So here in my valley, even on my own acres, I have a calendar of the earth's lifetime and a demonstration of the way this land was formed and shaped. Some of the rocks are strangers, carried here by the glaciers from far away; but the native rocks reach all the way back to the remote age of that Cambrian marble, which was here before there was one green plant on earth. There is igneous rock, quartz and flint, which was formed in the furnaces of the volcanoes. There is sedimentary rock of all periods, the cinder dust of volcanoes, the blown sand of cosmic gales, the lime from incredibly teeming primitive shellfish, the silt from countless rivers. There is metamorphic rock, the shattered quartz and disintegrated lavas and the fragments of limestone and sandstone that were crushed and fused into schist and granite by tremendous pressures. There are the crystalline rocks that settled out of the incredibly hot solutions of mineral salts that boiled up from the earth's bowels when time was young.

There they are, the materials of this earth and the stubborn chronicle of its lifetime, overlaid in many places with the thin layer of material we call soil which is seldom older than mankind. It is this thin and various layer, this film of arable soil, in which we plant corn and beans and grass and oats. There is the source of our day-to-day living, the source of everything we eat.

This, then, is the earth with which we live, the substance of this whole planet and the source of all living things upon it. In it are all the minerals the plants need to grow. By way of the plants, it feeds the animals, including man. It provides the basic materials for mankind's life and all his works. It is the storehouse and the pantry for life, and if we do not recognize that and co-operate with it we shall be in serious trouble no matter where we live. This is our environment. All our lives we shall be living somewhere on this earth, dependent on it. Every day, every hour, of our lives we shall continue to be in contact with it in one way or another.

Primitive peoples have always known this. Mythologies all the way back to beginnings speak of "Mother Earth." The early people always knew where they came from and where they lived. Throughout the ages, man has created trouble for himself every time he began denying this basic relationship and minimizing his dependence upon it. And time and again the forces of nature have quietly stepped in to force man back to proper recognition of these fundamentals.

There were the beginnings, and there at the bedrock of life are the continuances and the nearest thing we know to the eternities.

The Water

Oceans Around Us and Within

I WAS OUTDOORS all morning repairing fence, and, since the sun was warm and I was doing physical work, I sweated copiously. I provided proof that the human body is a porous skin sack filled with protoplasm and sea water. My normal activity, like that of any other human being, requires a daily intake of several quarts of water just to keep that body functioning. I can take that water as milk, tea, coffee, iced drinks or in many other forms, but I have to have it because this body of mine consists of about 120 pounds of water and only fifty pounds or so of other material. And I am constantly losing water that must be replaced. Like any other person, I could die of thirst in a relatively short time, though I could live for weeks without food if I had water.

I hesitate to say that there is any deep significance in it, but the proportion of water to solids in the human body is just about the same as the proportion of water to land on the earth's surface—71 per cent water, 29 per cent land. But these proportions may point to the fact that mankind originated in some form of aquatic life, some sea creature that learned to live on land. Certainly water remains an indispensable element in maintenance of life. Fortunately, there is plenty of water on this earth, though it is painfully scarce in some places and troublesomely abundant in others. Most places where man lives have a tolerable balance of it. My particular valley is comfortably endowed, though we do have floods and droughts on occasion.

Water is one of the simplest chemical compounds, two atoms of hydrogen and one atom of oxygen. It is present everywhere on earth in one of its three forms, as a solid or a liquid or a vapor. We think of it usually as a liquid, though every Winter it impresses itself upon our consciousness as a solid—ice and snow. In its vapor form it is all around us the year through, though seldom noticed. The water vapor in the earth's atmosphere tempers both the heat and the cold and creates our weather and climate.

If there were no clouds—all clouds consist of water in some form—our daytime temperatures would be intolerable and the nights would be almost as cold as the nights on the moon. And if there were no vast oceans and no ice caps in the polar regions, there would be no rain. Since all life depends on water, there would be no life.

Wherever the earth came from and however it was formed, our most remote evidence indicates that when it began settling down into its present form it possessed approximately the same amount of water that we know now. Apparently we have lost little or no water over the eons. We can explain this to our own satisfaction by saying that when water vaporizes from the seas and oceans and rises in the atmosphere it eventually reaches a place where cool air condenses it and returns it to the earth in the form of rain, snow or sleet. It seems unable to escape the earth's own atmosphere. We can thank the force of gravity for this.

Geologic evidence indicates that during the earth's first few hundred million years it was completely covered by water. If there had been no internal stresses, which heaved great land masses upward, it would still be covered with water to a depth of close to a mile and a half. Since the average elevation of the land is now about 2,250 feet above sea level, the seas must have vast and awesome depths. This is precisely what man's surveys have shown, tremendous undersea canyons, valleys and low-lying plains. In other words, the heights and extent of the habitable land are minor compared to the depths and expanses of the ocean beds. As I said at the beginning of this chapter, there is much more water than land.

Man, being a terrestrial animal, knows best the land and its relatively minor waters. You know best the hilltop town or the lowland farm where you live, the seashore or the mountains where you go for vacations. I know best this valley with the river and the brooks feeding it. It is the dominant geographic feature of my life, though because there can be no valley without attendant hills I am also keenly aware of the mountain that flanks one side of my river.

The river is flowing water. It rises in the hills to the north and it flows to the ocean to the south. Like all streams flowing into the ocean more or less at sea level, my river is salty for some distance above its mouth because the salt water of the ocean intrudes with every tide. But I live well above tidewater. The river I know day by day is fresh water, carrying only a normal amount of sediment and minerals in solution—and the customary amount of pollution in American streams.

But this river, pollution and all, is typical of all rivers in many ways. I get pleasure from having it close by, and I profit from it in minor ways. It somewhat tempers the climate, both Winter and Summer. In Summer it is the source of heavy dews which help water my fields and my garden. Any stream does these things. Because it is flowing water, it helps create eddies in the air along its whole valley. These eddies create wind currents. In Summer, for instance, there is nearly always a breeze in the valley, especially at night. On the other hand, on a hot, still Summer day the whole valley may swelter under a blanket of vapor—we call it high humidity, which means the same thing—from the river. In Winter the river's humidity can add authority to low temperatures and make a chill wind bitter. Occasionally its slight warmth changes a snowstorm into slush or cold rain. There have been times when higher land only two miles away, but out of the river's direct influence, received four inches of snow and this valley got no snow, but rain instead.

All these minor matters of weather are a result of the flowing water in the river and the vapor that rises from it. Just across the mountain to the northwest lies a small lake, a deep pool of still water. It, too, affects the weather in its valley. Summer nights along its shore are cool and breezy. Mild weather continues somewhat longer there than it does here, just across the mountain, because the lake's deep, still water tempers the air longer than does the flowing water here. But when deep cold strikes and the lake freezes over, it acts like an outdoor refrigerator for its whole valley. Its ice continues for weeks longer than does the ice in my flowing river, and in consequence its shores have a later spring.

Since the lake and the river are less than two miles apart at this point, the differences in their seasons and their weather are a striking proof of the effect of water which flows and standing water. Large rivers and large lakes create even more pronounced differences in their immediate areas.

Most of the water we know and use every day is fresh water,

distilled from the oceans by the natural process of the sun's vaporizing it. Vapor from the oceans is carried by the great air currents constantly flowing around the earth. It forms clouds which meet cold air masses flowing down from the arctic regions, the clouds are chilled and the vapor falls as rain. Only about one fourth of the rain which falls on the land flows back into the oceans through the rivers. The other three fourths is vaporized and makes more rain clouds or it is used by plants— grass, crop vegetation, trees, green and growing life.

Evaporation from the oceans is so vast in quantity that few of us can comprehend it. Those who study such matters say that about six and a half feet per year is sucked up by the sun from the Atlantic between 8 and 30 degrees north latitude, which includes Central America and Mexico. In the same belt of the Pacific about four feet of water is vaporized every year. Much of it returns to the oceans as rain, but the United States receives rain which, if spread evenly over the whole country, would be close to thirty inches each year. It isn't spread evenly, though. In one area of the state of Washington they get ten feet of rain a year. Where I live we average almost three and a half feet, a little over forty inches. In eastern Colorado, where I grew up, the yearly average is less than half that.

Pure water is almost unknown in nature simply because water is one of the best natural solvents there is. Water vapor is relatively pure, made so by the natural process of evaporation; but even the water in rain clouds contains various minerals in minute quantities because fine dust floats in the air and its mineral content is absorbed by the vapor. Rain which falls through a pall of smoke frequently contains a trace of sulphuric acid because it picks up sulphur from the coal smoke. We speak of rain water as being "soft" because it seldom contains the lime which "hardens" most ground water.

The spring water I use is relatively "hard," because it comes from seepage through a variety of rocks, including limestone. It also contains a minute amount of iron, copper and other minerals, all of them mildly soluble in water. It is these minerals which give water its taste. Distilled water, which is free of such minerals, tastes flat and insipid. Well water, no matter from what depth it comes, always contains a certain amount of mineral since it flows through layers of rock or sand to reach the point from which it is pumped. I have a shallow well which I have used on occasion, and a chemical analysis of its water is almost the same as that of the spring water. That is understandable, because it comes from the same general source and flows through the same kinds of rock. The deposit on the inside of a teakettle or any container in which quantities of water are boiled shows the presence of minerals in the water. Such deposits are a form of limestone, fine-grained and often as hard as marble.

Ice is nothing but solidified water. We happen to live on a planet where the normal temperatures keep most of the water in a liquid form. But that same normal temperature keeps another chemical compound, steel, in its solid form, and thus makes possible our whole industrial establishment. Steel happens to freeze into a solid at between 1100 and 1200 degrees Centigrade, whereas water doesn't freeze until it reaches zero Centigrade.

Ice forms crystals which are six-sided. In that sense, ice has some remote relationship to granite, the crystals of which are also six-sided. But the most familiar ice crystals are snowflakes, the fragile, feathery, evanescent flakes that came piling down on my valley last winter to a depth of eighteen inches in one storm. I went out in that storm and stood for fifteen minutes watching those flakes as they fell on the sleeve of my dark coat, and I didn't see two of them alike. I didn't expect to, for those who have made long studies of snowflakes and have examined and photographed tens of thousands of them say they have never seen two exactly alike. This infinity of pattern with a common basic form, the six-sided crystal, is awesome. I marvel at it every time the snow begins to fall, and I wouldn't think of trying to explain it. I doubt that there is any explanation. It is merely another example, and one that is perennially at hand, of the enduring mystery of even the simplest things.

When ice forms, even in the salty ocean, it forms as almost pure water, leaving most of the ocean's salts behind. Whaling ships short of fresh water have renewed their supplies and saved the lives of their crews by finding pools of melt on icebergs and barreling it for drinking water. Polar explorers melt polar ice for their indispensable water. I have never seen an explanation of this capacity of water to rid itself of mineral salts by freezing.

The very process of freezing water is complex. Water freezes, as we all know, at 32 degrees Fahrenheit, the equivalent of zero Centigrade. But perfectly still water can be lowered to much colder temperatures and remain liquid. Such supercooled water, however, will freeze suddenly if it is touched by even a needle or if a breath of air is blown across it.

One morning I went out at dawn to a small pool of water in the pasture. It was a completely still dawn, not a breath of a breeze blowing, and the temperature was 25 on the porch at the house. I expected to find a film of ice on the pool, but instead I found a fringe of paper-thin ice around the edges crisscrossed with long needlelike crystals. On the outer edges of that ice film, toward the center of the pool, were hundreds of such long, slender crystals thrust out over the surface of the still water. They went in every direction, some of them crisscrossing, and they were as much as four inches long.

I stopped at the edge of the pool and crouched down to look more closely. As I was crouched there a puff of a breeze came from somewhere, barely touching the surface of the water, not even noticeably rippling it. There was a faint but audible crackle, and a dozen ice needles seemed to shoot out from that

41

crystal fringe. In an instant, as that whisper of a breeze passed and gave the water an invisible brush, those new ice crystals formed before my eyes.

I waited there almost half an hour, and twice the same thing happened. But the water, because of the latent heat in the ground around and beneath the pool, was not cooled enough below the freezing point to crystallize completely. Finally the dawn breeze rose, rippled the water, broke the fragile crystals at the edge of the ice, and the critical time had passed. The air temperature probably had risen a degree or two.

It was the first and only time I ever saw such a thing happen, though I have often seen a shallow pool completely covered with a sheet of ice laced with such long needle-crystals, like reinforcement rods. And every winter I lift sheet ice from small hollows, such as a cow's footprint in the sod, and turn it over to see the intricate and often almost crude crystals on the under side. The upper surface is always smooth and milky from the mist of air bubbles, but the bottom of those small ice sheets is always covered with crystals, sometimes like the stalactites in limestone caves.

One remarkable thing about ice is that the water expands when it freezes. The expansion amounts to about 11 per cent in volume. Few other substances expand when they freeze; most of them shrink. But because of this characteristic of frozen water, the earth is habitable by man. Since water expands when it turns to ice, the ice floats. If it shrank, it would sink and our lakes, our rivers and our oceans would eventually be solid masses of ice. Liquid water would be a rare substance.

This expansion of water when it freezes also has been a major factor in shaping the land. Freezing water, that slow but inexorable pressure of forming ice, has gnawed away the mountains and will continue to do so as long as water freezes and ice melts. Frost is the most powerful and unremitting enemy of rock and the most persistent leveling agent that we know.

42

But it is in the waters of this earth, the clear, flowing liquid that covers so much of the globe, that we find the origins of life and the means of its existence. Geologists generally agree that the oceans originally were fresh as rain water, and that their present salinity is a result of eons of leaching and drainage from the land, and constant evaporation—in short, of the whole cycle of rain. In any case, the oceans now contain traces of virtually every inorganic substance known to man. They are the vast warehouses of the earth's raw materials, as well as the source of its life and the atmosphere which sustains that life.

A biochemist once said to me that my blood was nothing more than sea water polluted by organic material which we call red and white corpuscles. He smiled when he said it, but there is a large grain of truth in it. And that is true of all animal life. We are a strange and complex organization of flesh and bones that are bathed, irrigated and fed internally by fluids which are in some ways like sea water. Even the sweat which soaked my shirt this morning, the waste from my bodily processes that both cleansed me internally and cooled me by a process of evaporation, was full of the same salts as the ocean.

I think of myself as a fresh-water person, and my physical system will tolerate only a limited amount of sea water. But the affinity is there, nevertheless. The water I drink contains most of the ocean salts, inevitably, but in lesser quantities. The rain which nourishes my garden dissolves many of those same salts into a form which the corn, the cabbages, the tomatoes and all the other vegetables can use. The grass of my pastures is similarly nourished, and it goes to feed the beef I eat. My house is built of timber from trees that fed on water that came from the ocean, by way of the clouds. The cotton and wool of my clothing had the same ultimate source.

Man knows relatively little about water beyond what his charts and maps tell him. Where it came from originally is an enduring mystery, and why it remains here can be explained only in terms of our atmosphere and the terrestrial force of gravity. Man knows its chemical composition and its physical properties. He can make water out of two gases, oxygen and hydrogen, and he can separate water into those component gases. He uses water in countless ways. He can, though with only moderate accuracy, forecast when and where water will fall as rain or snow. But beyond these broad facts he really doesn't know much about water except that it runs downhill and that it is essential to life.

I, too, know these things, and I govern my life to a large degree by them. In the Spring I wait for the frost to go out of the ground so that I can plow and plant a garden. I plant when the moisture content of the soil is favorable to the sprouting of seeds. I trust to rain to water that garden, provide it with a sufficient amount of soluble minerals to make the plants grow properly. In the heat of the Summer, I hope for enough clouds to temper the strength of the sun for me and the growing things around me. If it is too wet, the plants may drown. If there is too much rain in too brief a time, the river will rise in flood. If there is not enough rain, the crops wither and my spring and my well will fail me and I shall be without the water my body needs each day. And in Winter my life and my mobility are eased or hampered by the amount of snow and ice that are the lot of this valley. The valley itself—its size and contours and fertility—is a consequence of flowing water that has been at work here ever since this land was lifted above the ocean bed. Water, which flows downhill.

As long as there is life here, there must be water. Water, though it is difficult to confine and is elusive in many ways, is accepted even by our sciences as an enduring and predictably constant element of the earth. It is used as the basis for computing the specific gravity, the relative weight, of most materials. It is the basis for metric measurements of mass and volume. It serves as the constant for the Centigrade system of measuring temperatures, which calls the freezing point of chemically pure water zero and the boiling point 100.

Life as we know it must have originated in the water. As it evolved, the plant and animal life of which we are closest kin emerged from the water onto the land, a dubious escape into another element. We are still here, living on the land, terrestrial creatures and terrestrial plants, but we have never really escaped. We carry the ocean within us and we perish without water.

The Air

Breath of Life

YESTERDAY the barometer here in my study showed exactly 30 inches of atmospheric pressure. This morning it stands at 29.7 inches. The pressure is falling. From long experience, we know that when the atmospheric pressure falls we probably are going to have stormy weather, very likely wind and rain. That is one of the things we have learned about the actions of the air around us. That air, which the specialists call the earth's atmospheric envelope, creates our weather and most of the varying conditions of our life.

My barometer reminds me every day that I am a peculiar kind of finless, gill-less fish living at the bottom of an ocean of air. I cannot swim in it, as a fish swims in water, but it is my element; as I move about on this air ocean's floor I am partially supported by it and its oxygen feeds the fires of my life.

46

Theoretically, I could move more freely in a vacuum; but my body would explode in a vacuum even before it suffocated. Air pressure holds me together.

I cannot see the air around me. It is invisible to me, and I cannot even imagine the kind of eyes that could see the atoms that compose it. A fish can't see the water, either. I do see drops of water in the air, and the fish sees bubbles of air in the water, but we are in a sense equally limited. We both, however, have learned to live with such limitations.

This ocean of air which surrounds the earth acts in many ways like an ocean of water. It has waves and eddies and currents and swirls. But because the air is a gas and the water is a liquid there are also profound differences. Water is much heavier than air; otherwise rain would never fall from the clouds. Water is of almost the same density from top to bottom except in the greatest ocean depths, and even there the change is slight. Air is much more dense at sea level than it is even on a two-mile-high mountain, and it thins away to almost nothing at extreme heights. And air is a mixture of gases which vary from place to place and change completely at different altitudes. At sea level the air generally consists of about 78 per cent nitrogen, 21 per cent oxygen and small amounts of water vapor, carbon dioxide and occasionally hydrogen and helium. At high altitudes the oxygen is displaced by hydrogen, and at extreme altitudes even the nitrogen is displaced by the hydrogen. About seventy miles above the earth virtually the whole atmosphere consists of hydrogen. From there on up the hydrogen thins out into empty space.

We sometimes think of it as a fortunate circumstance that oxygen is heavy enough to permeate the atmosphere down here where we live. That, of course, is nonsense. We are here because this is true. We evolved as we did, and all life exists in its present form, because the oxygen is here, not the other way around. The oxygen wasn't put here for us to use. We just happen to be a form of life that grew in an atmosphere rich in oxygen. It takes a bit of imagining, but there may be other forms of life elsewhere in the universe that live on hydrogen or some other gas.

All the visible life we know requires oxygen to sustain its life processes, and it gives off carbon dioxide as a waste material. This process is called respiration. We are familiar with it in animals. We never see plants breathe, but they respire in the same way, consuming oxygen and giving off carbon dioxide. But in green plants another process, photosynthesis, also occurs; and photosynthesis consumes carbon dioxide and gives off oxygen. It is the solar-powered process by which plants manufacture starches and sugars, their basic foodstuff; and chlorophyll, the green coloring matter in leaves, is its principal agent. Water and carbon dioxide are absorbed and converted to carbohydrates, and free oxygen is released. These two basic life processes—consumption of oxygen in respiration, and consumption of carbon dioxide in photosynthesis—roughly balance each other. Because photosynthesis releases oxygen, man—who consumes oxygen—is most at ease, physically, and in somewhat better health when he lives in a wooded, grassy area. To a degree, the fires of man's own industry tend to smother him because they use his vital oxygen and create clouds of carbon dioxide.

When we use the expression "the fires of life" we are not merely using a figure of speech. All animal life is sustained by a process of oxidation. My body temperature, which is just beyond the mid-point between the freezing and boiling points of water, is a result of quiet fires smoldering inside me. They are quite different from the cool phosphorescent fire in a firefly, because my fires do create measurable heat. In a sense, I am a kind of heat engine, for this process creates the energy to drive my nerves and muscles. The harder I work, the more energy I use, the more fuel I have to burn. The more we force those inner fires, the more oxygen we need. The only place we can get oxygen, unless we are under an oxygen tent in a hospital, is from the air we breathe. So when you or I work hard we breathe deep and fast to get more air into our lungs, more oxygen for the body.

Aside from this constant, unremitting need for the oxygen in the air, man is eternally at the mercy of that air in other ways. It creates all the weather we know. It filters the sun's rays. It serves as a reservoir of latent heat. It insulates the earth's crust. Sometimes this air is a benevolent environment, and sometimes it tries the soul and buffets and tortures the body. There are times when I wish I could get away from the air's ungovernable tantrums, but I know there is no place to go. I am a prisoner of this thin, invisible envelope that wraps the earth. Even if man does eventually get to the moon or some other planet, he is going to have to take some of this imprisoning air with him to survive.

The air is a gas, and like all gases it acts according to "laws" which we have discovered and codified. For instance, all gases expand when they are heated and they shrink when they are cooled. Lord Kelvin, the British physicist, found that gases expand almost one third when they are heated 100 degrees Centigrade, and he set up a scale of expansion of gases. This is called Kelvin's Law, with typical human arrogance. It isn't a law any more than the fact that the sun rises every morning is a law. It is a precise statement of what happens. But we call such statements "laws" because we like to lay down rules. Such "laws" make it easier to understand what is happening and to predict what will take place under certain conditions. When we have written down enough of these "laws" we have what we call a "science," which is nothing more than a body of knowledge about how one particular department of nature insists on acting.

Air, like all other gases, expands when it is warmed. When it

49

expands, the same volume of air weighs less than it did before. It rises. As it rises, it leaves a kind of pocket in the atmosphere. Cooler air begins to flow into that pocket, since air flows somewhat as water flows. This flow of air is a wind, since wind is nothing more than air in motion. If the air was warmed swiftly and if there was a large quantity of it—if, in other words, a large empty pocket was left—there is a strong rush as the cold air flows in. This creates a storm, perhaps even a hurricane.

The polar ice caps are constantly creating large masses of cold air. The tropical regions, constantly heated by the sun, continually heat large masses of air. With this warm tropical air constantly rising and the cold polar air constantly invited to flow into the void, one might expect steady north winds in the Northern Hemisphere and south winds in the Southern Hemisphere. But other factors are at work. Irregularities of the land surface—mountains, plains, river valleys, lakes—divert the air currents. And the spinning of the earth on its axis, west to east, creates all kinds of complications. This spinning of the earth drags some of the air along with it, especially that relatively close to the ground. But the inertia of the atmosphere makes the upper air, that at high altitudes, lag behind and flow—or seem to flow—in the other direction, east to west.

So there are at least half a dozen major forces at work on the movement of the air, and countless minor forces. The major forces create climate and the big storm systems which dominate weather. Climate is the long-term average of the weather, and weather is the day-to-day condition of the atmosphere. I sometimes think that I put up with the climate and that I live with the weather.

The weather I live with is governed primarily by the seasons and the movement of storm centers across the land. Those storm centers, as a general rule, move across the United States in a seasonal rhythm, roughly seven days apart in Summer and five days apart in Winter. This variation is caused by the temperature differences, Summer and Winter, because Summer storm systems consist of warmer air, which is more sluggish than the air of Winter storm systems. This rule is rough, at best. If it weren't, we could expect the same weather on Sunday of each week, and on Wednesday and on Saturday, through the Summer season. Some Summers it seems to work that way, with rain every weekend. But eventually the sequence is broken and a new pattern sets in. And the same is true of Winter. The five-day sequence went haywire one Winter and we had a snow-storm every weekend for two months, a typical seven-day Summer cycle. It became very tiresome before that sequence was broken, but it finally skipped a weekend and formed a new pattern.

The day-to-day situation is complicated here in my valley by the land contours and the river. The river, like all water, warms up more slowly and cools off more slowly than the land. And the river's temperature warms or cools the air above it. The mountain, with a good deal of exposed rock, warms and cools quickly, and it, too, affects the temperature of the air above it. So there are breezes here in the valley, morning and evening, and some-times there are strong, gusty winds created by these strictly lo-cal conditions. In the heat of the Summer, which happens to be the growing season, the river remains warm at night and creates a good deal of water vapor. The mountain cools off swiftly after sunset and creates a cool mass of air which flows downhill by gravity. That cool air not only makes it more comfortable to sleep, but it strikes the river's water vapor, chills it, and cre-ates a heavy dew. Since the vapor extends out over the valley, and since the pasture and the vegetable garden are in the lower parts of the valley, that dew is as good as a light rain night after night. In dry periods it keeps the pastures green and nurtures the sweet corn, the beans, the lettuce, the tomatoes and all the other garden truck. It is a sort of built-in sprinkler system. All river valleys and most lake shores have it in some degree.

Because the air is invisible we usually forget that it has substance. But it does. Otherwise there would be no wind and if there were wind it would have no force. And if it had no substance, neither birds nor airplanes could fly. They can't fly in a vacuum, not as long as they are within reach of the earth's pull of gravity.

It is the substance of the wind that makes a sailboat possible and operates a windmill. A windmill is nothing but a turbine driven by air instead of water, or steam, or any other fluid or vapor. And because warm air is lighter, less substantial, than cold air, the Winter wind is stronger than the Summer wind. Tests prove that a wind of the same speed exerts 25 per cent more force in January than it does in July. That is because there is more body, more substance, to the air in cold January than in warm July. That is also one reason a dog pants and a workingman breathes faster in Summer than in Winter. They have to get more air into their lungs to get the same amount of oxygen out of it.

The substance of the air also is responsible for sound. Sound is vibration, and vibration sets up rhythmic motions in the air, which are picked up by our ears. Sound travels faster in thin, warm air than it does in thick, cold air, but it sounds louder in cold air because more of the vibrations are transmitted. At zero Centigrade sound travels 1,089 feet per second at sea level, and its speed increases about two feet per second for every degree rise in temperature. There are other variables, such as humidity, but they are minor. When I see a flash of lightning five seconds before I hear the thunderclap I know that it was about a mile away. If I catch the tingling scent of ozone after a lightning flash I don't have to count. I know that bolt was too close to suit me. Ozone is another form of oxygen, three oxygen atoms in one molecule, formed by a flash of lightning or other electricity through the air. You don't smell the ozone when the lightning is a mile away.

Most of the evidence seems to indicate that the air in the earth's atmospheric envelope is only a remnant of what was there in the most ancient of days. All the water on earth came from that original atmosphere. So did all the coal, the oil and the gas. The carbon in the coal, oil and gas and in many of the rocks was taken from the original atmosphere by the plant life, and most of the nitrogen in the soil was also put there by growing plants. Since the earth is generally conceded to have been one of the hot spots in the universe in its early years, and since hydrogen and oxygen combine to form water in the presence of intense heat, the formation of all the earth's water from the mixed gases of the atmosphere seems not only plausible but inevitable. A large part of that primitive atmosphere, that superheated swirl of gas which began to solidify several billion years ago, turned to water. It absorbed some of the heat in the process and the earth began to cool off and take form. Eventually it cooled enough for life to appear and begin to evolve in what we now speak of as a hospitable atmosphere.

It is natural for us to speak of it as a hospitable atmosphere, but when I examine such a statement closely it seems strangely twisted. We constantly tend to put the consequence on the wrong end. The air wasn't put here for us to breathe. We evolved as air-breathing creatures, grew up in the air, adapted to it, learned to survive in it; our bodies evolved, without any help from our slowly emerging minds. And, for all our achievements, we haven't changed the atmosphere in any noticeable way.

When I consider the bland assumption that the world was made for man, I wonder if my dog doesn't believe I was put here just to feed and house him and make him reasonably comfortable. It would be no more absurd than for me to think the world was made for my comfort and convenience or the air was put here, in precisely the right mixture, just to give me the proper amount of oxygen to live in physical comfort. The really marvelous coincidence, if you care to call it that, is that the human lungs, the blood and all the organs and tissues are so perfectly adapted for life in this gaseous environment.

It is remarkable how the human body adapts itself to the air around it. Indians who live in the high Andes, where the air is thin and the oxygen content low, not only have larger lungs than lowland Indians but their blood is different. The high-altitude people have more red corpuscles in their blood than the lowlanders. Red corpuscles carry oxygen from the lungs to the rest of the body. So those high-mountain Indians not only have bigger bellows, lungs, with which to breathe in the air, but they have more oxygen traps, red corpuscles, to capture and carry the oxygen to their tissues. Apparently this change, this bodily adaptation, is a natural means of meeting the local needs of their environment. But it remains a flexible arrangement. When one of these high-mountain people is taken down to sea level, the number of his red corpuscles gradually diminishes to about the proportion found in sea level natives. He doesn't need those extra oxygen carriers, so his body dispenses with them. When he is taken back to the mountaintops, the red corpuscles increase again.

The ability of the blood to absorb oxygen from the air in the lungs comes, as was stated before, from the presence of hemoglobin in the red blood cells. Hemoglobin has a loose affinity for oxygen, captures it in the lungs, and carries it throughout the body. As the hemoglobin distributes the oxygen, it picks up carbon dioxide and other waste materials and carts them away.

To repeat, hemoglobin—really, its chemical basis, which is named hemin—has a structural resemblance to chlorophyll. Chlorophyll is the active green substance in leaves which takes water and carbon dioxide from the air and changes it into a starchy form of carbohydrate which the plant needs for food. The principal chemical difference between the chlorophyll of the leaf and the hemoglobin of human blood consists of a few atoms of iron in one and a few atoms of magnesium in the other. Replace the iron atoms in hemoglobin with magnesium atoms and you have, in chemical terms at least, chlorophyll. Both substances use air as the agency for their vital processes; one uses the oxygen from it, the other uses the carbon dioxide.

The amount of carbon dioxide used by plants is almost as surprising as the amount of oxygen used by animals. It has been estimated that the carbon dioxide in the air over one acre of land is only enough to produce four 100-bushel crops of corn. And it has been estimated that if all the land area of the earth were planted to sunflowers, those sunflowers would use up all the carbon dioxide in the air in just a little over four years.

Such calculations, of course, are purely theoretical. The amount of carbon dioxide in the air is constantly being replenished by the animal life on earth, just as the oxygen supply is being replenished by the plants. There is no imminent danger of a shortage of either oxygen or carbon dioxide. Even in the oceans, the incalcuable quantity and diversity of both plant and animal life maintains a balance of these two essential elements.

Some of the long-range forecasters occasionally get excited about the air and its components. Now and then one of them says that when the human population of the earth doubles its present number there will be less oxygen per person, perhaps even a shortage of oxygen. I haven't yet heard anyone say that there was a shortage of carbon dioxide in past millennia when the plant life on this planet was so prolific and the animal life was just getting well started. Yet that would be just as logical, just as true.

Actually, there seems to be little variation in the character of the air from one century to the next. If there is, nobody had discovered it the last time I looked. The fundamental changes in the atmosphere occurred a long time ago, before anyone was here to know what was happening. Billions of years ago. There

55

probably haven't been any major changes since the first form of life appeared, certainly none since there was dry land and life upon it. This air we know is, as a mixture of gases, one of the most stable and unchanging things on earth today. Man certainly hasn't been able to do much to it except add some very unhealthful strontium atoms. He has been able to use it in a thousand ways, but he has never been able to tame it.

Air, the lightest, most pervading and yet most elusive element of his environment, dominates man's life from conception to death. We speak of birds as being creatures of the air, but so are we, groundlings though we are. Deprive us of air, or remove the oxygen from the air for a few hours, and we would become a vanished species. Not only man, but all forms of animal life.

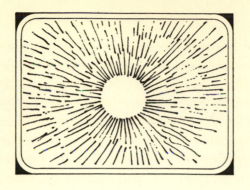

Fire

Flame of Creation

THE GREEKS called fire one of the four elements, and in a fundamental sense they were more nearly right than those who later insisted that fire was only a chemical reaction. Our earth must have been born in fire, it was shaped in fire, and without the inconceivably hot blaze of that swirling mass of fire we know as the sun there could be no life on earth. We even have our share of fire within us, at the core of our own vitality. Whether fire is an element or not, it is elemental.

When I study the history of man I am repeatedly reminded how closely man and fire are linked. Not earliest man, who was a beneficiary and sometimes the victim of fire but had not yet tamed it and made it his own. But man somewhere along the early path of misty speculation, before he left the caves but after he quit the treetops, somewhere along the route to the most primitive of stone implements. A paleontologist turns up a fossil bone and traces of charcoal carbon from a fire and he tells himself that he is on the track of ancient man. He feels sure that his find is no longer an ape or some type of pre-man.

But fire goes back far beyond the first appearance of man. Those who speculate on the origins of the earth believe that it began as a swirling cloud of fiery gases, fired with the vigor of atomic reactions. It swirled and burned, they say, and slowly it consolidated itself as the gases were transmuted in that ancient fire and became a core of solid matter that one might term ash. It wasn't the ash we know. It was a kind of atomic ash, perhaps, atoms stripped largely of their energy and come to rest as basic metals, possibly something like the meteorites we know, though even heavier and more substantial. We do not know what is or ever was at the core of the earth.

But the atomic fires burned, in this gaseous cloud, for eons, and the elements were separated and combined and consolidated, and the earth began to take form. Out of those fundamental fires came all the rocks we know and rocks we have never seen nor ever shall see, hidden deep in the earth's dark center. Out of them, too, came those lighter elements, the gases which envelop the earth and are known to us as the atmosphere. And the continuing fires wedded oxygen and hydrogen, forming water. Thus the oceans were born, in the primitive fires.

All this required more centuries than man can count knowingly, but eventually this earth, this relatively solid planet, took shape and its atmosphere began to stabilize. But the fires still burned, inwardly. Rocks deep in the heart of the earth continued to burn and the waters over them continued to boil. Earthquakes convulsed the planet. Volcanoes erupted, spilling oceans of lava which kept the seas boiling and vapor and dust clouds thick overhead.

And eventually, perhaps a billion and half years ago, there was a kind of balance with a core of rock, a covering of water, and a gaseous envelope of atmosphere. The seas were still warm. The land was still submerged. And into this warm oceanic water came the first germ of life. Where it came from nobody knows. It came. We accept that fact. Perhaps it came in a meteorite. It may have arrived here in some form of microscopic dust that drifted into this new world's orbit. Some now believe that it generated spontaneously in the warm, mineral-rich seas. Whatever the origins, it came, found a hospitable home, and multiplied.

That was the beginning of life. It prospered, and it somehow achieved its own variations. Perhaps the slow changes were adaptations to the cooling of the water as the fierceness of the earth's inner fires abated. Perhaps they were responses to the elemental food supplies, which in that remote beginning were the minerals dissolved in the water. Water, the great solvent liquid of creation, can retain a varied mineral content as its temperature varies. In the fiery youth of the earth, much of the water must have been a rich chemical soup. It probably was not as salty as it is now, but it must have been rich in other minerals. And as the chemical content of that primitive water varied through the ages, any life dependent on it had to change its diet or perish.

Several of the early forms of known life still persist. One is a microscopic fleck that lives on an iron salt, extracts it from the water, eats a part of it and builds the residue, which is pure iron, into microscopic tubes which become homes for whole colonies of these minute creatures. Scientifically they are known as Leptothrix, from the Greek for "small hair." Leptothrix is found today in and on the margins of mineral springs with a strong iron content. There it builds its iron-tube colonies into visible masses that look like rusty yellow slime.

At one time the leptothrices were numerous not only beyond counting but beyond comprehension. They laid down, in those microscopic iron tubes, all the iron ores of this earth. They built the vastness of the whole Mesabi Range. They were responsible for those once-rich ore beds within five miles of my house, from which Salisbury iron was made in the youth of this nation, iron for the cannon of the Continental armies, for the great chain across the Hudson, for the try-kettles of Hudson River whalers, for the bell-toned, four-foot Salisbury kettle that stands in my barnyard as a watering trough for the cows.

There are no numbers to count the iron-eating leptothrices, nor the allied bacteria of the same era which lived on manganese and sulphur and other minerals in that warm sea of the earth's childhood. But there they were, warmed and proliferated by the fires of the earth. And they changed, or others of their kind changed and evolved, as the heat of the inner fires altered. Out of their kind came plant and animal to populate the earth.

The fires continued, inwardly. There were earthquake convulsions, and there were volcanic upheavals, lava spewed through the seas. Land was upthrust, and swallowed by the waters, and upthrust once more. And eventually continents began to appear.

Some say, with what seems to be valid reason, that it was the fiery upheaval that eventually brought the first of the ice ages. Vast clouds of volcanic dust, say these theorists, swept the earth and thickened the atmosphere. That dust cut off the sun's blazing heat. Ice began to form, fed upon itself. Then the dust settled, the air cleared, the sun shone hot once more upon the frigid earth. The ice melted. That, at least, is the theory, and there is much evidence to back it. Alternate ages of active volcanoes and overwhelming ice are written in the rocks, and with that record is the evidence of vast, long-continued showers of volcanic dust from time to time.

But eventually there were continents, or at least huge areas of low-lying land clear of the lapping oceans. And there was life to swarm over that land. Much of the land was tropical, washed

by warm seas and made steamy by the blazing sun in relatively
clear skies. Life swarmed as never before, but most abundant
was the plant life which reared itself in swampy jungles of tree
ferns and other giants of that age. Plant life grew in every moist
pocket and marginal swamp. It grew and fell into the muck and
created huge peat beds.

Overhead the rain clouds gathered, and as such clouds always
do they created the million-volt tensions of electricity that exploded in lightning bolts. The searing explosions split the sky
and lashed the earth. When they struck in those swamps of
heaped and drying vegetation, they set fires that swept the peat
beds. Fire burned the surface tinder and charred the underly-
ing mass. That char sealed off those bottomless peat bogs from
decay and insect hunger. The land was submerged. Sand flowed
over it, and depths of water, and the convulsive earth squeezed
and pressured that primitive peat into the anthracite we know
today.

That was perhaps 300 million years ago, but we still see, in
our clouds of factory smoke, the oblique benefits of those light-
ning-set fires of the distant past. Without those fires, which
sealed the raw materials of coal, we would have no coal to burn
today. Fire was a factor in its creation; fire is its result today,
controlled fire, tamed fire.

When and where man obtained fire is one of those mysteries
that will forever remain unsolved. It was available to anyone,
of course, and had been available since the beginning. But man
was the first form of life to capture it and put it to his own use.
All other forms of life either avoided fire or perished in it. Fear
of fire is instinctive in the animal. Yet somewhere back at the
beginning, man captured a spark of fire and made it his own,
perhaps at first using it only to defend himself from those enemies who never learned that fire could be tamed. A fire in the
mouth of a cave was as effective against the natural enemies as

a wall would have been, perhaps even more so because snakes could not penetrate it nor could insects pass through fire with impunity.

The legends hold no clue. Primitive peoples believed that fire was the possession of the gods and that it was stolen for man by some mythical hero, often a friendly animal. To the ancients, fire was sacred as an earthly manifestation of the sun. The records, even in mythology, are scant. The early Greeks worshiped it. Vesta was the goddess of the hearth, and the vestal virgins were committed to guard the sacred fire. When a new colony was established, fire from the sacred fire in the metropolis was taken there, thus linking the colony to the mother city in a practical as well as a spiritual tie.

But Greece came late in human history. There were centuries of man's mastery of fire before the first Greek was born. And we know little of those centuries except that man and fire were linked, that man's progress must have been along a path warmed and lighted by fire. He learned early to strike fire from stone, perhaps by accident in chipping his earliest crude stone implements. Not too long after that he must have learned to create fire by friction, for the fire drill reaches far back into the mists of antiquity.

With fire, man could move out of the cave. He could carry fiery walls of protection with him and he could somewhat fend off the cold. He could move about the earth, for fire gave him safe mobility as well as strength beyond his own thews. In time, it gave him the first advance beyond the raft for water travel. Fire made possible the hollowing of a log, man's first primitive boat. And fire gave man eyes to see in the darkness of night.

One must marvel at the courage of the first man to hold fire in his hand. How did it happen? Was he stunned by the concussion of a lightning bolt, and did he rouse and grasp a brand from the flaming, lightning-struck tree and discover that the flame at the far end of that brand could be carried away? Lightning seems a more likely source than the volcano, which rained death as well as fire. However it happened, that first man to capture fire and hold it at arm's length conquered not only his own impulsive fears but the far deeper fear of punishment by jealous gods who owned all fire. Who was he? We shall never know. Prometheus came late, and even the origins of the Promethean tale do not reach far back into the mysterious dark of the unreachable past.

One can with little qualification say that the history of fire in man's hands is the history of human civilization. It gave him protection, it gave him warmth, it gave him mobility. Eventually it gave him metals and mechanical power. It created industry and made man the master of many—but by no means all—natural forces.

I think of man's invention of speech as the greatest invention of all time, for it was the means of shaping and communicating and preserving thoughts and ideas. But among all man's conquests, the greatest was the capture and taming of fire.

There is another form of fire than the visible flame, however, a form more fundamental to life, all life, than any fire that ever burned at a cave's mouth, on a hearth, or in a forge. That is the slow, quiet fire of living, the burning of food in the oxygen of the intaken breath.

My life depends on the temperature of that inner fire. Lower that temperature a few degrees for any length of time and my body begins to die. Raise it five degrees and I am critically ill; raise it ten degrees and my life processes burn out and I die. Starve those inner fires of oxygen for a few minutes and they begin to flicker.

This is true of all forms of animal life, though the temperature of normal living varies from species to species. It is true even of insects, of reptiles, and of fish. They all need oxygen to feed some form of that inner fire.

And it is true of plants, though the vital fire in the plant

63

kingdom is both complex and obscure. During daylight hours the plants use sunlight and carbon dioxide and water to manufacture food, and they give off oxygen, apparently with little of that silent, inner, oxygen-fed fire of life. But at night, in the absence of sunlight, the plants use oxygen. Their dim fires burn in the darkness, and since they do not use that heat to maintain inner temperatures as animals do, they throw it off as waste. It is simply the heat of oxidation of food in the plant's normal processes of living. Scientists have measured the heat generated by many plants and they find that it increases sharply at the time of germination and at the time of blossoming. Plants, like animals, have their time "in heat."

I see this each year, when the early plants begin to grow again. It is most notieable in the bog just down the road where skunk cabbage grows in the muck.

The skunk cabbages, the Old Men of the Swamps, sprout early. Often they appear while the bog is still locked in ice. They thrust up purplish-brown hoods with a strong green undertone, fat and primitive-looking. Inside that hood is a large, bulbous "spike" of blossoms ready to open. Soon after it opens, the big green leaves appear.

Sometimes in January, often in February, I find the skunk cabbage thrusting up literally through the ice. Always there is a small circular patch of melt around the persistent shoot, even if the temperature is in the low twenties. This baffled me until I learned that skunk cabbage, with its intense vitality, generates its own heat, sometimes as much as twenty-seven degrees higher than the temperature of the surrounding soil and air. Its urgent time of blossoming stirs the inner fire, the heat is concentrated in a closed conical dome, and the frozen soil and the ice above it make way for the fire-fed urgency of green life.

Somewhat the same thing happens in my own flower garden, where there is always a thawing area around the first shoots of iris, daffodil, tulip and other early risers. They, too, have their fires of Spring. They burn the food within them, somewhat as I burn bread and meat, and the energy it creates is released by them in the form of heat.

The fires in animal life are more pronounced. Regardless of outside temperatures, the human body maintains a temperature level of approximately 98.6 degrees, though that varies somewhat from one individual to another. The body temperature varies somewhat with the species, too. The normal temperature of a horse is 100 degrees, that of a dog 101.5, that of a sheep 102.3, that of a rabbit 103.1. In birds the temperature is consistently higher, as high as 108 in some species.

Bird temperatures fluctuate from day to night and to some extent throughout the day. Birds are so active and have such a high metabolism that they have to stoke their inner fires almost constantly. At night, when they are at rest, the temperature may drop four or five degrees, and in the hummingbird, which is so small and so active, there is even a kind of hibernation at night, when the fires burn low and all bodily processes go into low gear. Whippoorwills and some other birds that live entirely on flying insects also have the ability to go into a semi-hibernation where the fires of life are dampered, the body temperature drops, and they can live for days on a minimum of stored fat.

Zoologists attribute this capacity for diminishing the vital fire to what they call "imperfect warm-bloodedness," a kind of recession to an intermediate stage of evolution from reptile cold-bloodedness to the warm-bloodedness of bird and mammal.

But most warm-blooded animals, including man, have reached an evolutionary point of no return. They cannot, even temporarily, resume the low-fired cold-bloodedness of their remote ancestors. They have been so completely and irrevocably adapted in all their vital processes to warm-bloodedness that their fires must glow continuously. The hibernating woodchuck's temperature may drop to 43 degrees and he will survive and resume his full activity, but man and nearly all other warm-blooded creatures could not long tolerate even a small fraction of such a bodily chilling.

Oxygen is the burning element for these inner fires, and carbohydrates are the major fuel. As they burn, they yield energy. But the heat of the body seems less for personal comfort than for swift and efficient progression of vital chemical processes. The warm-blooded creature may be said to live swiftly. Much of the heat and the energy is produced by nervous impulses, the remainder in all likelihood by muscular tensions. These necessities dictate the metabolism, the intensity of the chemical processes. When we say that we are "burning up energy," we come close to literal truth. We are using nervous and muscular energy that is created by the inner fire. That fire, however, continues even when we sleep, although nerves and muscles are presumably at rest. Our vital organs are still at work and, to some extent, the nerves are still on the job. Our sleep is not hibernation.

One might say that here is the basic necessity of life—the continuing inner fire. All living creatures are constantly undergoing combustion, burning up. Yet there is a constant replenishment of the fuels for that fire, so that until disease interrupts or old age slows down the process of replacement, we are never being consumed.

Man has long dreamed of a perpetual-motion machine, some contrivance that he could set going and confidently expect to go on forever. But man himself is such a machine. So is every form of life we know, which consists of some combination of substances animated by the vital spark and endowed with the inner flame of energy. Grass and all vegetation lives on and on, lit by the fire of life and passing on that fire by seed and germination. Birds are such "machines," perpetuating life and motion in the fertile egg. And man, energized all his own life by

66

that inner flame, passes it on to each succeeding generation with his own seed, the ovum and the sperm, out of which grows another sentient individual, another complex heat machine which eats and grows and thinks and reasons only because of that quiet inner fire.

Life—
The Green World

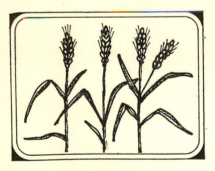

Plants

Elemental Food Factories

IN THE BEGINNING there was life, simple, single-celled life that undoubtedly lived in the water because water is the natural habitat of the most primitive life we know. The beginnings of life are mysterious, as are almost all its early changes. We can only speculate about what happened. But there is every probability that the very earliest form of life was not yet committed to be either plant or animal. It was in that unresolved state where the balance could tilt either way. Eventually some of the individuals in that welter of uncommitted life turned one way and became animals, some turned the other way and became plants. Some never made the commitment; they persist, even today, in that anomalous state which defies the classifiers but does provide evidence of the way life must have been many millions of years ago. From those that did make the commitment—"decision" is too strong a word—came the two great branches of life we know today, the animals and the plants.

Broadly speaking, the plants found a way to manufacture and store food from elemental substances, and animals found that they could subsist by eating plants or other animals. The plants became the manufacturers, the animals became the consumers.

How these changes came about is completely unknown. Somewhere along the way the plants evolved chlorophyll, the substance with which it became possible to convert water, carbon dioxide and salts into nourishing food with the help of sunlight. This was a major achievement, and it still baffles the researchers. Some borderline instances still defy classification. There is, as an example, the strange bit of life called Volvox.

Volvox is classified as a colonial flagellate. It consists of a colony of cells arranged in the form of a minute sphere, barely visible to the naked eye. It lives in the water. It moves by waving the hairs on its surface. It contains chlorophyll. It also contains germ cells which are of two kinds, approximately male and female, and which maintain the species by sexual reproduction.

Volvox is classified by the zoologists as a kind of animal. Botanists also claim it as a kind of plant. It manufactures food from inorganic material. Yet it moves about like an animal, and it has other resemblances to the simplest forms of animal. And Volvox is not unique. There are other borderline cases, down there at the simple beginnings of life, where the identity, plant or animal, is difficult to determine.

In a sense, plant life and animal life complement and even sustain each other in a remarkable manner. Plants, making food by photosynthesis, consume great quantities of carbon dioxide and give off great quantities of oxygen. Animals, in the simple process of breathing, consume oxygen constantly and give off carbon dioxide. We might call this a fortunate circumstance, because it provides the essentials for both forms of life. Or we

72

might say that the two forms of life evolved simply because the essentials for living were available and it is the way of life to use what is at hand. This, of course, leads down that blind alley of the meaning of life, the purpose, and I have no intention of getting lost there. I am quite sure that no one yet knows either the meaning or the purpose of life, and I am content to accept life as a fact and go on from there.

Back toward the beginning, then, original life diverged in form and became animal, on the one hand, and plant on the other. The earth as we know it today probably could not continue to support either form of life alone. Eventually the carbon-oxygen balance would be upset and the whole complex, interrelated system of life would either revise itself or perish.

Among the very earliest traces of plant life are fossils from the Cambrian rocks, which are about 550 million years old. These plants were a form of algae, very simple water-dwelling plants. We still have algae, which form the basis of most of the green scum that gathers on stagnant water in late Summer.

The earliest fossils of land plants come from the Devonian period, about 350 million years ago. Some of them have neither leaves nor roots, though they are definitely land dwellers. They resemble seaweed in many respects; seaweed is generally regarded as the ancestor of all the plants we know today. Some of those early land plants consisted only of underground stems and a few uplifted shoots, some of which bore spore cases. Often those uplifted shoots were naked, but occasionally they had scales that took the place of leaves, much like the scales on today's club mosses. These plants have been identified as plants in transition from algae and seaweed toward ferns.

The transition was relatively swift. Land plants soon began to show leaves like elementary fern fronds. Then they grew swiftly in size. There was a kind of explosion of plant life, the vitality too tremendous to be contained in one or two types. Hundreds of variants appeared, some of them of great size. By

73

the Carboniferous period, some 300 million years ago, there was a profusion of towering fernlike plants. Some were trees 20 feet in circumference and 150 feet tall. Some had long, grass-like leaves that grew in spirals up the trunk. Some were much like giant forms of the running pine and ground cedar that grow today as creepers in my own woodland.

The reasons for this profusion of form and giant growth are obscure. The time was just before the rise of the giant reptiles, the dinosaurian families. Clearly, there was some combination of conditions that favored life as never before, life in many forms and life urged to giant size. Perhaps there was some form of obscure but benevolent radiation. Perhaps the climate was more than usually hospitable. Perhaps there were newly available salts in the earth, the water and even the air that promoted such growth. Nobody knows why it happened, but the fossils prove that it did happen. The earth teemed with life, both plant and animal, and that life was more than usually fertile in variations.

Among the giant plants of that era were huge horsetails, much like the Equisetum or scouring rushes that grow today along my riverbank. The scouring rushes I know today are seldom more than three feet tall, but the giants of those ancient days were taller than my sugar maples. Those early equisetums reproduced by spores, even as the scouring rushes of today do. The spore system was the primitive one, and it still persists. But among those long-ago jungle forests were a few seed ferns, venturers in a new direction. Some of them had fronds like today's spleenwort, and they bore seeds like quarter-inch hazel-nuts. Those were among the very first true seeds, still a minority among the agents of reproduction at that time.

Nobody knows exactly when it happened, but the original plant line diverged into two major families, the true ferns, which never abandoned the habit of reproduction by spores,

74

and the seed-bearers, which pointed toward all the flowering plants we know today.

The next great step came during the Jurassic period, which began about 155 million years ago. In fossils of that time are trees closely related to the ginkgo of today and trees that obviously were ancestors of today's sequoias. But even more important were the smaller plants and bushes that were beginning to show flowers and something like the modern seed-bearing apparatus. Those plants were the forerunners of the daisy in my meadow, the laurel on my mountainside, the sumac that tries eternally to take over my pastureland.

Again the evidence is obscure and there are many gaps, but it seems clear that another explosion of plant life was beginning. The form and habit of trees, bushes and lesser plants were changing swiftly, in terms of geologic times, and the varieties were proliferating. Perhaps there is no clear connection, but it is worth noting that by then the first birds were flying through the forests, the early mammals were scurrying through the underbrush. Animal life, too, was changing rather swiftly. Giant ferns and other transitional trees were thinning out or vanishing, and the giant lizards were specializing toward their doom and disappearance. In the animal world, placental birth and the mammalian way of life were taking over, and among the plants the blossom and the seed were coming into their own.

The blossom is difficult to trace. Some of the early cycads—the cycad was a tree midway between a tree fern and a palm in appearance, and a few examples have persisted down to today—bore cones six inches long, elaborate cones, complex and clearly transitional. These cones had both pollen and ovules. The male cells had hairs on them that propelled them to the female ova for fertilization. The cone sheltered this intricate process. The result was a true seed-bearing plant. The cone itself probably was the beginning of the flower we know today.

Somewhere between those early cycads, with their elaborate cones, and the primitive pines and firs of the next period, the Cretaceous, which dates from about 115 million years ago, the explosion of plant life was completed. Fossils from the Cretaceous rocks show a much elaborated and extended range of plant life. In it were the early ginkgos and sequoias, but also trees and shrubs that clearly belong to families we still know—magnolias, cinnamon trees, oaks, sycamores, poplars. And most of the modern flowering plants were already established and recognizable.

The links between those plants, evident in rocks of more than 100 million years ago, and the primitives of only 35 million years earlier, are almost completely missing. The line of descent from those Cretaceous plants down to the present is relatively clear. We can follow that line forward. We cannot follow it back with any degree of certainty. We cannot even be sure that the primitive cones of the early cycads actually did lead to the blossom of, say, the magnolia of today. It could be that the cycad cone never evolved far beyond its early stage, and that the magnolia blossom was a wholly new and different development. We do not know. All we know is that there were the very early trees, in great profusion, most of them ferns and spore-bearing, and that there were primitive ventures into a seed-bearing system of reproduction. Of this there is clear evidence. Then there is a gap, which is followed by sudden and extensive evidence of seed-bearing plants, a tremendous profusion of them. And those seed-bearers were the ones which inherited the earth, the seed-bearers and the mammals.

The spore-bearers did not vanish, any more than the fish vanished, or the amphibians, or the reptiles. They did retreat to a lesser position. They persist today in the form of ferns, mosses, horsetails, club mosses and fungi. But their dominance is gone.

There are many basic similarities between plant and animal

76

life. The structure of both plants and animals has at its core the fundamental protoplasm, the substance of the cell. Both have systems of utilizing food, creating new protoplasm and other cell materials and developing the energy needed for the life process. Both reproduce by some form of self-division, usually in the form of the seed. The seed in the plant is the equivalent of the egg in the animal. In it are contained all the elements for producing offspring from the parent, and the mysterious agents which make that offspring substantially the same as the parent. And both plants and animals have the capacity for adapting themselves to their environment.

Plants, however, are not endowed with the means of movement which enable animals to move about in their environment. Because plants can find their necessary food in one place, they remain in one place. They have roots, which anchor them and which draw from the earth many of their essential food elements. They have leaves, which capture both light and moisture from the surrounding air. Although they seem to have nothing like a nervous system, they do respond to certain sense stimuli. Some are notably sensitive to touch.

The most notable characteristic of plants is that they not only gather their own food but manufacture it into usable form. And they store both food and energy. The chief agent in this manufacture is chlorophyll. Endowed with chlorophyll, the plant can convert inorganic materials—carbon, hydrogen, oxygen, nitrogen, and various other minerals in small quantities—into sugars, and it can store these sugars in the form of starch. It also can store solar energy for use during the night and during heavily clouded days. In the process of manufacture, the plant absorbs water and carbon dioxide, and it gives off water vapor and oxygen. It is this capacity for manufacturing and storing food which makes the plants so vital to the whole animal world. Animals can eat only organic matter, and the greater part of the world's animal population lives on plant life di-

77

rectly. The flesh-eating animals live on plant-eating animals, so there is total dependence on plants.

Plants respond to temperature in somewhat the same way that cold-blooded animals respond to it. For most plants there is a rather clearly marked temperature zone in which any particular plant can live. Those we call annuals cannot survive the cold of a normal temperate-zone Winter, so they entrust their life stream, their persistence as a kind of life, to seeds that can survive a degree of cold that will kill the parent plant.

Perennial plants in most instances have means of coping with cold weather. Deciduous trees shed their leaves in the Autumn and withdraw much of their moisture and food into their root system. In a sense, they hibernate; their whole process of living and growth slows down. In many of the perennials, however, and even in some of the annuals there appears to be a color system which comes into action in the early Spring. The shoots of the red osier dogwood, for instance, turn warm red before the leaf buds open. The lilac leaves that appear first are deeply tinged with purple. The first hood of the skunk cabbage is brownish purple. The swamp maple's buds are red. There are many instances of such early-Spring coloration, particularly in the temperate and arctic areas. There is even a variety of oxalis whose leaves are a strong purplish red on the under side and conventionally green above. This oxalis grows in deep shade, and on overcast days the leaves fold up to reveal the red side, though on sunny days those same leaves open flat, their green surfaces exposed to the light. Is it not possible that here we have examples of plant coloration designed to trap extra heat, or some other form of radiation, at a time when the plants are in need of an extra burst of energy? Perhaps.

Plant reproduction is achieved in many ways. Nearly all plants reproduce by seeds or spores, though many also reproduce by cuttings or other division of the parent, and many have bulbs or tubers or runners that travel either underground, as some grasses do, or aboveground, as strawberries do. The most elaborate means are by seed, and the most involved seed systems are in the flowering plants. Some plants are asexual, needing no pollination. The dandelion is an example of this, though the dandelion uses both the sexual and asexual systems, more or less depending on circumstances.

Pollination calls for the presence of an ovary, or a female organ, and a stamen, or a male organ. The pollen, equivalent of the male sperm in the animal, joins and fertilizes the ovule, equivalent of the egg in the animal. Together they produce the fertile seed. Pollination is achieved in various ways but always by some transport of the pollen to the ovule. Insects are the transporting agent in many cases; birds sometimes do the job, hummingbirds in particular; wind carries much pollen; water carries pollen to some aquatic plants. And gravity is at least a contributing agent in such plants as the field corn that goes to feed our cattle and hogs.

The fertile seeds are distributed in hundreds of ingenious ways, all designed to scatter the seeds away from the parent plant and populate a wider area. The wind carries such seeds as those of dandelion, thistle, poplar and cottonwood trees, even the seeds of maple and elm trees. Seed-bearing cattail fluff is borne for miles on the wind, and so is the silky fluff of milkweed. And in the West the wind rolls tumbleweeds across the plains, scattering ripe seed at every bounce.

Birds carry many seeds, particularly those with a pulpy covering. Berries have seeds that go through a bird's digestive tract unharmed and are planted with the bird's droppings. I see each year young cedars growing along my wire fences, planted in the droppings from birds that fed on the dark berries of the cedars in the groves on my hillside. Some animals also distribute seeds in the same way, particularly cattle and horses. Last

Spring I spent hours pulling mustard out of a pasture, mustard that grew from seeds in manure from a herd of cattle that had been fed hay cut from a mustard-infested field.

Hundreds of wild plants spread their seeds by encasing them in husks equipped with hooks and spines. Each time I take a Fall walk in a weedy area I come back with an assortment of burs and stickers on my trouser legs, everything from burdock to beggar ticks, from needle grass to cockleburs. And all grazing animals carry such seeds from one place to another. In the West where I grew up there was a creeping plant we called devil's claw that had a twin-horned seed case four inches long, each end of it equipped with a claw that could pierce boot leather. Cattle and horses sometimes were lamed by these vicious claws, but they carried the seeds far and wide over the plains.

And many plants have means of shooting their seeds. The wild geranium, so plentiful and so beautiful in my area, ripens its slim, pointed seed pods with growing tension. When they are fully dry, a chance touch or even the wind itself can set them off, and these pods open as with a minor explosion, flinging the seeds several feet. The witch hazel seed case opens with such explosive force that it can fling the seeds twenty feet or more. A plant called touch-me-not explodes its seed case in much the same way. And some wild beans have spiraled pods that open, when fully ripe, with a twisting snap that hurls the beans several feet.

All these methods are, as we say, designed to disperse the seeding, to scatter the plant's offspring. Perhaps "designed" is not the correct word; but the effect is the same. The seeds are dispersed, the species is spread, and there is a better chance of survival because some of the seeds probably will land in a spot suited to their growth.

It would be convenient, and it would be satisfying to man's sense of inquiry, if we knew exactly how and why plants came into being. But we do not know. We have evidence of certain primitive plant forms, and we have clues to the general line of evolution and change. We know a great deal about modern plants, and by comparison we know more and more about plants that throve millions of years ago.

We know the basic plant processes. We can even trace the chemical changes that take place in photosynthesis, the process of transforming simple raw materials into sugars and starches through the agency of sunlight and chlorophyll. We have yet to break down the basic secret of chlorophyll itself. And we still do not know that fundamental secret, the ultimate nature of the nucleus of the cell, that central core of all life, whether it be plant life or animal life. There it remains, the eternal spark of life, the mystery that is transmitted from parent to off-spring, that carries with it the nature of the child, the kind of being that child will become, whether it is a radish or a wren.

But here we are in a world teeming with plant life, a world full of animal life dependent on the plants. Each Spring we see that plant kingdom renewed with sprout and shoot and bud and flower. The green and growing miracle is a perennial won-der to all of us who look upon it. And the details of that plant world, the grass, the tree, the shrub, the succulent plant, are relatively well known. Yet no one yet has solved such a simple mystery as why the petals of a buttercup are yellow or why the violet is purple. We make up answers, but even the best of those answers are incomplete.

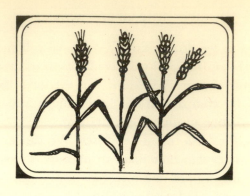

Grass

Earth's Benevolence

WHEN WE DWELLERS in the North Temperate Zone think of the green world we usually think first of grass. Grass grows almost everywhere except in the deepest woodland and on the most parched desert. Where trees straggle or can gain no foothold, grass flourishes and possesses the earth. Wherever there is soil, moisture and a few weeks of Summer warmth, grass will grow.

Man is more dependent on grass than on any other species of plant life. He could do without trees, though he would suffer sorely for want of shade and fuel and lumber. He could do without flowers, though he would be deprived of color, of beauty, of fragrance, and of certain items of food and fiber. But without grass he would surely starve. The cereal grains are all grasses—corn, wheat, oats, rye, rice, barley. The pasturage for his meat animals is grass. Grass anchors the earth's soil against erosion. Grass cools the earth and constantly renews the oxygen in the atmosphere. Grass is indispensable for life as we know it.

Grass is among the humblest of all the visible forms of plant life, even though its seven thousand species do include such a giant as bamboo. Few ordinary grasses grow more than three feet high, and most of the grass that clothes our great plains and flatlands is even shorter. Yet it is so insistent, so vigorous in growth, so proficient in reproduction, that it outpopulates all other plants. Perhaps someone has counted the number of individual grass plants in an acre of ordinary pastureland, but I have never seen the figures. They must run well into the millions.

As plants go, grasses are relatively simple. Perhaps it would be better to say "simplified," because the grasses go about their job of living and multiplying with notable directness and have the relatively complex mechanism for such living stripped down to essentials. Most grasses have fibrous roots that seem to reach out at random yet tap a considerable area of soil. Their stems are jointed, growing in segments, one on top of another. Their leaves are long and slender, with parallel veins; they grow from the joints of the stem, clasp the stem part way, then spread their full breadth free of the stem. Their flowers are simple, consisting of stamens and pistils without petals or sepals, but they are surrounded by bracts, stiff, leaflike shields which in many species project as spikes or beards. The seeds are compact, hard, dry, and they carry the germ at one end, with the remainder of the seed consisting of concentrated food; it is this food concentrate that makes the cereal grains so valuable to man. And grasses have an unusual capacity for replacement of lost stems and leaves; this makes pasture grasses and forage crops invaluable to the herdsman because a meadow or a hayfield tends to replenish itself.

83

The fibrous roots of wild grass lace the soil so completely that they form a turf or sod. Throughout the West of my boyhood such sod was cut and laid up like bricks to build the walls of countless houses and barns, even corral walls to confine livestock. The sod of the plains substituted as building material for the logs of the forest lands. Such sod sometimes was so thick and tough that it required four horses to pull a plow turning a single furrow through it.

The grass of the High Plains, the vast pastureland of America, was so plentiful that for generations it supported herds of buffalo estimated at 100 million or more. For thousands of years those grassy uplands fed those herds and the grass was never noticeably diminished. Then cattle and sheep followed the buffalo and, though some areas were overgrazed, the grass persisted until men with plows ripped up the sod to plant wheat—another grass, by the way, but a nurtured, civilized grass without the staying power of buffalo grass and all the other wild ones. Drought diminished the wheat crops and wind blew the dust, but after the dust storms had somewhat abated the grass crept back into the plowland, as it always does. Man can destroy the grass, but if he turns his back for a few years nature urges the grass back where it belongs. Grass is persistent. Grass has an affinity for the land. Grass can and will, if given half a chance, repair the damage man does to the green earth around him. Here in my own lush valley the grass would take over my garden patch in two years if I left it to its own urgencies.

Grass is such a minor form of plant life and has so little "skeleton" that only minor evidence of it is found in the rocks. We know next to nothing about its origins and only a little about its history. During the Miocene epoch, when the Great Plains were being slowly lifted out of the seas, the common reed, one of the grasses, apparently was growing in the marshlands all across the American continent. And one of the cord grasses, a marsh grass common in salt marshes, spread its roots and stems, trapped silt and converted vast marshlands of the Midwest into the deep, black soil that covers much of the area from the Alleghenies to the High Plains. The grasses were here long ago, helping to build soil and hold it against the wash of rain and the abrasion of wind. And except for those grasses which constitute the great bulk of our farm crops, grass is largely unchanged from what it was when man first looked around him and knew that the natural world was green and hospitable for him and his own kind.

All the cereal grains and most of the forage grasses that man uses were evolved from wild grasses. It is in the field of grass culture and evolution that man has made his greatest impress on the plant world. And even that impression has been made only over the past few thousand years. We think of agriculture, the growing of useful, chosen plants, as an old industry; but when one thinks of the big time span it is very recent. Agriculture probably began, at the earliest, toward the end of the last ice age, which was at the most some 25,000 years ago, and possibly only half that.

Wheat is probably one of the oldest of all cultivated plants. It is known to have been grown in the Mediterranean basin about six thousand years ago. A wild species probably much like the ancestral type still grows in Palestine and Syria. The wild wheat grass of the American West is a related species, but today it is used only for forage. Wheat as we know it was first brought to America by the early colonists, and for a time it was displaced in American farming by the native Indian corn, or maize.

Rice, which was developed from a native wet-land grass in the European and African warm zones, was being cultivated in southern Asia at least five thousand years ago. Wild varieties are also native to America, especially in the marshes, both salt and fresh, from New England to Texas. It is also found in the fresh-water marshes of North Dakota.

Barley, a native of southwestern Asia, was to the early Romans what wheat is to Americans today. It was widely grown and used as a breadstuff, especially for soldiers and workmen. It is still widely grown both in Europe and in America. In Europe it is a food grain, but in America it is used primarily as feed for livestock and in the manufacture of malt for brewing purposes. Several wild grasses of the barley type grow here in America, the best known of them being called squirreltail grasses. The quack grass, with which I am at war in the garden every year, is related to the barley tribe.

Rye is a native of the Mediterranean area and was known to both Greeks and Romans, though they did not cultivate it. It did not come into general use as a foodstuff until after the Middle Ages, when it became an important food grain in Russia, Germany and other parts of northern Europe. We also have a wild rye grass, though its relation to the cultivated variety and its wild ancestors is dubious.

Oats seem to have been native to eastern Russia. They were cultivated in Europe before the Christian era but were not grown by the early Greeks or Romans. Wild varieties of oats still grow in Iran, Arabia and northern Africa. There is a wild oat grass, apparently native, which still grows in the Central and Eastern states of America.

The millets, used in Asia and Africa as a food grain but grown in America primarily as forage, fodder, and grain for poultry, belong to a family with many wild cousins. Crab grass, the common lawn pest, is one of the millet family. The foxtail grass that grows along my roadside and is beautifully red and amber at seed time is a wild millet. The bur grass that fruits in small, spiked burs and clings to my socks and trousers when I prowl roadsides and waste places, is one of the less welcome members of the millet family. Each Winter I feed pecks of tame, cultivated millet to the birds at my feeding station. It is a part of most wild-bird seed mixtures on the market.

Sugar cane is a big grass native to India. It has been cultivated in India and China since the earliest days of recorded history. It is distinguished by the high sugar content of the juice in its stems. Long culture and persistent breeding for high sugar content seem to have robbed it of its own fertility. Its pollen is seldom potent, so it has to be propagated by cuttings.

Probably related to sugar cane, though distantly, are the sorghums and broom corns, which are native to tropical Asia and Africa. We have no wild sorghums. In the Northern states of America both sorghum and broom corn are grown for livestock fodder and sometimes for the straw of the broom corn heads, from which brooms are made. In the Southern states the sorghum stalks are the source of a sweet juice from which syrup is made. This syrup was the sorghum, the common sweetening of the back country, used by American pioneers.

Maize, which is corn to most Americans, is a true American native, though its ancestor is lost in the mists of the past. It had been hybridized and selectively bred and grown for centuries before the first white man arrived in America. Apparently it originated in Central or South America, possibly in Mexico; but it was growing in such varied latitudes and climates as the Andes, the semideserts of our own Southwest, the warm lowlands of Florida and the cool, stony soil of New England when the first white settlers came. As a food, it is the most important contribution the American Indian made to the world.

Botanists and plant hybridizers still marvel at Indian corn and search for its ancestors. A native Mexican grass called teosinte appears to be the closest relative yet found, but other ancestors probably include South American "pod" corn and Tripsacum, a wild plant native to both North and South America. How the various crosses were made, and when, still baffles the

87

investigators. But the most primitive corn yet found and the earliest records of it in ancient art show both a plant and a cob of grain much like those we know today except in size. All we really know is that corn had been grown here in America in a diversity of varieties long before Europe knew that America existed. Modern plant breeders have extended its growing range and greatly increased its yield, but they had an already tamed grain, a mysterious hybrid of complex ancestry, to start with. Corn, incidentally, is one of the few true grasses with a solid stem. Most grasses have hollow stems.

Bamboo is the largest of all grasses, the tree of the grass family. Most of the bamboos are native to the Old World tropics, but America has one wild member of the family, the cane reed that is found in swamps from Virginia to Florida and along the Gulf Coast. Bamboo grows to a hundred feet in height. Cane reed sometimes grows thirty feet tall. It forms the canebrakes of our Southern swamplands. It also furnishes the cane fishpoles most of us used in our childhood. The young sprouts of bamboo are edible and are eaten like asparagus. Bamboo fiber and wood are used for almost everything from building to papermaking, especially in the Orient.

The tamed grasses feed man and his livestock, and some of them provide shelter for him. He couldn't live without them in any degree of comfort or plenty. But it is the wild grasses that have done most to shape this world, this place where man lives. And they go right on shaping it, day after day. Occasionally man co-operates, but for the most part the grasses need little help.

A river comes flooding down to the ocean, bearing a load of silt that it drops at its mouth. Over the years that silt becomes a sand bar. Marsh grasses, their seeds carried by the water and the wind, take root there and grow and slow up the flow of the water, and the water drops more silt. The sand bar widens, becomes an island. The grasses grow and die and form humus, the substance of fertility. Bushes take root, and trees. What was first a sandbar, then an island, becomes a barrier at the mouth of the river. It creates a marsh. The marsh thickens, traps more silt, fills up with decaying vegetation. Eventually it is a new part of the mainland, simply because grass came and took root on a sand bar.

Wind whips the sand at the shore of the ocean or a big lake. The sand piles into dunes and the dunes begin to spread inland. Then a dozen seeds from perhaps ten miles away are carried there by the wind. They germinate, take root, grow and spread. They creep up the side of the dune, slow the wind and begin to anchor the sand. The first few green blades become a sparse green covering. Their roots form a mat. The grass traps dust. A covering of humus and topsoil is slowly created. What was a shifting dune becomes a grassy hillock, and the spread of the dune is ended.

A brook in my pasture rips out a gash in a Spring flood. For a few weeks the gash stands raw and open to the weather. Then the grass begins to reach with its roots, down over the face of that flood-torn scar. The roots take hold, new stems rise in the sun. By Summer's end the grass has softened and clothed the scar and the roots have begun to form a new anchor for it. It eases the bite of Fall rains and somewhat checks the erosion of Winter snow melt. Another Spring and the grass spreads on down the bank to the brook's edge. The grass catches seeds of wild geranium and field mustard and forget-me-not. Another year and it is a waist-high tangle of urgent growth, and if I would not have it spread back into the pasture I must get at it with scythe or sickle. But if I were not so intent on neatness and my own plans for this land, in another five years it would be a burgeoning brush patch, all because grass roots must reach out and occupy the vacant soil.

Give a grass seed a roothold and it grows, even on a rock. I have seen grass growing on a ledge where three years before there was nothing but a patch of lichen. The lichen caught drifting dust and formed a film of soil. Moss came to occupy that soil, and it in turn caught more dust, more soil. Then a grass seed fell there. And the grass penetrated the soil with its roots, found sustenance, and endlessly searched for a tiny crack in that fundamental rock. Rootlets found a crack, worked their way inside, fattened and wedged at the rock. Moisture followed the roots, and frost found the moisture, turned it into the most persistent, most powerful of nature's small wedges, the ice crystal. The rock was pried apart.

That is the sequence in rocky places—the lichen, the moss, the grass, then a bush, a tree, and crumbling rock. Thus are the ledges reduced to rubble, to stones, to sand, to silt, to the soil that fills the valleys and nurtures the fields of man, the harvests of man's chosen grasses, the cereal grains.

Grass spreads in a multitude of ways. Some grasses multiply by underground stems, which send up new shoots at every joint. Some multiply by runners aboveground. But most of them spread by seed. Grass seed is often so small that it is easily carried by the wind. Often grass seed has tiny, buoyant hairs that catch the air currents and ride them surprising distances. Investigators gathering insects and other forms of life from airplanes have trapped grass seed almost a mile above the earth. One grass introduced into Louisiana from South America sixty years ago now is found from Virginia to California, gone wild and spread by its own devices.

Some grasses have spines on their seeds that attach themselves to passing animals and hitch rides to new areas. Sheep, with their thick wool, are constant carriers of grass and weed seed into new territory, but cattle, horses and even wild animals do the same thing to some degree. Some grasses, like the berries mentioned earlier, have tough seeds that resist digestion and are carried from place to place in bird droppings. And man has unwittingly carried grass seeds all over the world. Several African and Caribbean grasses came to North America 150 years ago in the bedding used on slave ships and the feed used on ships carrying cargoes of livestock. All the old trade and caravan routes were lined with strange, exotic grasses, carried there from far away by man and his animals. And alien and often unwelcome grasses have come to new territory, still come, in fact, as impurities in imported seed. A strange millet related to our native foxtail grasses appeared in a field of millet planted from seed imported from China in 1932. Fifteen years later this alien was found, self-spread, all the way from New York to North Carolina and west as far as Nebraska.

The living habits of grass are, in one sense, much like those of the social insects. Grass grows in communities wherever possible, usually in communities of literally millions of individual plants. Unlike social insects, however, grass makes no division of labor, has no social organization within the colony. Each grass plant is complete unto itself, a unit, capable of doing all things necessary to its own process of life. It is simply a plant that colonizes, as trees colonize a woodland. One rarely finds a lone grass plant, and if one does he may be sure that there will be others soon, for grass is prolific. Where one plant can live, more will follow.

Nearly all plants have a strong capacity for self-renewal, but grass is outstanding in this respect. Break off or cut one stem, and another stem will soon rise to take its place. Mow a hay-field, and within a week there will be new growth from the shorn grass plants. Even such relatively temperamental annual grasses as our cultivated cereal grains will persist in growing and coming to seed if they are cut or grazed off early in the season. Corn, which is probably the furthest removed from its wild source of all cereal grains, is the least adaptable in this respect, but I have known a field of corn to be eaten off part way by cattle early in its growth and still recover and produce a crop of ears.

The wild grasses are notably persistent. I have cut quack

grass down to the root repeatedly through the season, and still it sends up a few seed stalks and comes to its own fruition. And one year's damage seldom checks the next year's growth of a perennial wild grass.

It is this persistence of life and growth that has enabled the grasses to take and hold such large areas of the earth. Every Spring I marvel at the urgency of all green things, but I have a never ending wonder at the vitality of the grass, all grasses. Their simplicity of flowering, their toughness of seed, their essentially simple organization of parts, are all remarkable and a vital element in their persistence. But it is this indomitable urge to live, this insistence on growing and seeding and multiplying, that indelibly impresses me. The grasses are as ubiquitous as the insects, and they have that same tenacity of being. If one can say that any form of visible plant life possesses the earth, that plant life is the grasses.

Flowers

Pollen and Seed

THE FLOWERING PLANTS are often spoken of as the most advanced form of plant life, with the blossom itself as the evidence. In this sense, the flowering plant is the plant world's equivalent of the mammal in the animal world.

I am not sure that I can agree with this unless the word "advanced" is taken in a rather restricted sense. Man has a habit of calling any complex form of life or complex life process advanced, with the clear implication that it is better or more admirable than its predecessors. From man's point of view, the highest achievement of evolving life is man, with his intricate arrangement of cells, specialized organs and members, elaborately complex nervous system and remarkable brain. But the very simplest forms of life still persist. They may never have "advanced" very far, but they proved long ago that simplicity can endure and that it long, long ago solved the basic problem of life, which is to live and reproduce. Man, endowed with intelligence and strong emotions, has other ideas about the purpose of his own life, but we have yet to verify any purpose in nature beyond life's own persistence. And in that sense, the blossom on a buttercup or on an orchid is no more than a complex means of continuing life from one generation to the next. This should not lessen man's aesthetic or intelligent interest in a flower, but it does mean that man, not nature, invented aesthetics.

Since the original division of primitive life into the two branches, plant and animal, there has been relatively little change in the basic processes of living, maintaining life. To repeat, plants manufacture their food from inorganic substances, using the sun's energy to convert air and water into sugars and starches; and animals maintain their life processes by consuming organic matter, plants and other animals. These are fundamental processes that have been elaborated but not basically changed over hundreds of millions of years.

But the processes of reproduction, though based on a common fundamental, have diverged in many directions. This has been particularly true in the plant world, with the most complex reproductive mechanism of all in the blossom.

Stripped of detail, the fundamental of reproduction is a division of the original life form. At its simplest, the single-celled plant or animal divides itself, nucleus and all, into two parts, both of which grow and in turn reproduce, always by self-division. As one moves down the eons of life history, this self-division becomes more and more complex. In both plant and animal the parent individual, itself an elaborate organization of cells, achieves the power of creating special reproductive cells which are separated from the parent and grow into new reproductive units. Essentially, this is still a form of self-division. In animals this special reproductive cell is the egg. In plants it is the spore or seed.

In most instances, the egg or the seed must be fertilized before it can grow. Fertilization is accomplished by the union of two dissimilar cells, the egg and the sperm, each produced by a separate parent, the female and the male. This necessity and this differentiation of cells and parents constitutes sex. The word "sex" comes from the Latin and seems originally to have meant to cut, to divide. It really means that there is a difference between the two parent organisms, the male and the female.

In animals and in most insects the male and female cells are produced by separate individuals. In some plants this is also true, but in many plants both the female and the male cells are produced in the same flower or in different flowers on the same plant. If a flower produces both kinds of cells it always has both the female and the male organs. In a sense, the bisexual flower, which produces both kinds of reproductive cells, is one of nature's economies, a simplification of the basic means of reproduction. The simplification, of course, is in the method, not the means, since any flower is a complex of specialized organs.

There is a scientific explanation of the seed-egg process that is important to the specialist and perhaps interesting to the layman. This interpretation is called "the alternation of generations." It points up the idea that life is continuous even though it passes through a variety of forms even in the same species. It applies to all forms of life except the very lowest, the single-celled. Perhaps the most graphic example is in the life of a butterfly, which proceeds through the form of egg, larva, butterfly, then egg again. Each of these forms constitutes a "generation" and each is quite different from the others. Yet all are necessary in the life history of a butterfly.

In a flowering plant there are equivalent steps. The common field mustard, a weed in the pastures of my valley, is a green and leafy plant which forms a cluster of buds at its tip and comes to blossom in May. The mustard flower has four small yellow petals and is bisexual, with one pistil, the female organ, surrounded by six stamens, the male organs. In the ovary at the base of the pistil are produced special female reproductive cells or ovules. In the anthers at the tip of the stamens is produced the pollen, the male reproductive cells.

According to the alternation-of-generations interpretation, the individual grains of pollen, the male cells, are short-lived individual plants, though they are unable to reproduce alone. And the ovules, the female cells in the ovary, are also short-lived individual plants also unable to reproduce alone. They constitute a "hidden" generation in the plant's life.

When these minute male and female plants, pollen and ovules, meet and fuse, they produce a fertile entity, the seed. The seed in turn will grow into a leafy, budding mustard plant, and when its yellow blossoms open the whole process will be repeated. In this sense there is an unending continuation of life which passes through alternate forms, generation by generation. And the flower, the blossom, is no more than a mechanism for producing those minute "plants," the pollen and the ovules, which join to form the seed.

To the paleobotanist this interpretation explains, at least in part, the basic process of evolution. Plants, all life, apparently originated in single-celled ancients. In even the most complex plants and animals of today, life still goes through that primitive form where minute flecks of parent life divide and unite in the creation of the seed or the egg. Male sperm and female ovules are created by the parent. These two basic units, the male and the female, must unite to create a more complex unit, the fertile egg or seed. Unless they meet and fuse, they cannot duplicate the parent and carry on the life process, including reproduction.

Broadly speaking, the female cells, the ovules, are quiet but hungrily receptive bits of life. They remain in the flower's ovary awaiting the arrival of the pollen, the male element. The ovule's

96

whole purpose, as far as we can comprehend purpose, is to be fertilized. The male pollen is vigorous and active. In one sense, the pollen is a spore. Its purpose is to find an ovule and fertilize it. This impulse of necessity in both ovule and sperm is one of the most urgent and yet one of the most persistently hidden of all the life processes, since it usually occurs at the microscopic level.

An excellent example can be found in any cornfield, on my neighbor's farm or in my own sweet-corn patch. Corn produces its pollen, its male cells, in the tassel at the tip of the plant. The ovules, the female cells, are on the young ear farther down the stalk. The ovules are ranked on the cob, hidden beneath several layers of husk; but each ovule, each potential kernel of corn, has a long "silk," a hollow strand of soft vegetable fiber that reaches out into the open at the tip of the ear.

At a proper time, the pollen is mature and the ovules are ready for fertilization. The pollen begins to fall from the tassel. Gravity urges it downward and the breeze distributes it. One grain of that male pollen, one spore, falls on the tip of one strand of silk. It is held there by a kind of adhesive. The tip of that silk is an ideal place for growth of that particular kind of spore. It grows into a male plant too small to be seen by the naked eye, a plant that thrusts a fine thread down that hollow silken strand toward the waiting ovule. That pollen grain, that spore, is endowed with enough energy and urgency to thrust that thread eight inches or a foot down that silken tube to reach the ovule. The ovule is reached, male and female cells fuse, fertilization occurs, and a kernel of corn begins to take form beneath the protective husks. The female ovule extended its silken invitation. The male pollen grain found that particular silk. In a matter of hours pollination, fertilization, had been accomplished. A fertile seed, from which another corn plant can grow, had been created.

This elaborate process has been evolved over millions of

years. It began with the first plants that crept or were washed by the waves onto land. They were spore-bearers. The spore itself was a result of long evolution, a means of dividing the parent plant without destroying or greatly impairing the strength of the parent.

The spore is minute, often microscopic, and it is not always distinguished by sex. In the simplest form of spore plants, an intermediate form of plant grows from the spore, a bisexual plant, and from that plant is reproduced still another plant substantially like the original spore-bearing parent. Mushrooms are among the most prolific of the spore-bearers, a single mushroom often producing two or three billion spores. Mushroom spores are sexed, but they can scarcely be called male and female because there are four "sexes" among them and they will pair off only in certain groupings, say number one and number three, or number two and number four. In a favorable environment these spores grow into minute filaments, and if two filaments of the proper "sexes" meet they fuse and grow into a mushroom capable of bearing more spores. But the unmated filaments that grow directly from the spores are plants, intermediate forms and an essential part of the whole reproductive process. They are broadly equivalent to the pollen grain with its searching thread thrust down the corn silk and the waiting ovule at the base of the silk.

Many plants still reproduce by means of spores. Most of them are water dwellers, but ferns, horsetails and fungi are among the land dwellers that cling to the spore system. Spores of most water-dwelling plants have hairlike means of movement, but the spores of most land-dwelling plants have no means of self-movement and usually are distributed by the wind. And most of them go through an intermediate stage of individual growth before they re-create a plant like the parent. The fern spore, to take one example, is more direct in its process than that of the mushroom. The fern spore grows into a tiny, inconspicuous plant called a prothallium—from the Greek words meaning "before" and "young shoot"—and the prothallium has both male and female organs from which a plant like the parent fern is eventually produced.

No one knows exactly why or when the primitive spore-bearing plants moved over toward the process of reproducing by means of a fertilized seed, but by the Carboniferous period, some 300 million years ago, there were trees that had begun to produce seeds. Apparently a plant of the fern type condensed the intermediate generation, the growth of the spore into a bisexual prothallium, and created a cone in which the essentials of this process could take place. Out of this evolved the fertile seed.

The blossom of a plant has only a few essentials. There is the pistil, the female organ, equivalent to the ovaries and the uterus of the female mammal. In it are the female cells, the ovules, awaiting fertilization. And there are the stamens, the male organs, equivalent to the testes in the male mammal. They produce the sperm cells, the pollen, full of urgency to find and fertilize the ovules.

Those are the essentials. They can be found in notable simplicity in the inconspicuous flowers of most grasses, many of which consist of little more than an ovary and three stamens. The grasses have achieved this simplicity because they are pollinated by the wind and need no assistance from insects or birds. More complex blossoms, especially those depending on insects for help in pollination, have elaborate sepals and petals. The sepals are the leaflike outer coverings of the flower, often the bud sheath, and in some ways resemble leaves. They may have evolved from leaves. Usually the sepals are green and have chlorophyll in them, just as do leaves. The petals are the divisions of the corolla, the cup which usually surrounds the pistil and stamens.

Some flowers have no sepals, some no petals, but the great elaboration and variety of floral forms have been in petals and sepals, in their shapes and colors. Some flowers have nectar to lure insects. Some have deep pockets in which pollen or nectar or both are hidden so that the visiting insect must invade or reach inside to get the treasure, and thus unwittingly leave pollen from another flower to fertilize the ovules. Some have their stamens and pistil so arranged that the insect visitor simply releases the pollen for self-fertilization. Whatever the arrangement, the blossom's design seems dictated by a need to insure pollination of the ovules.

The whole architecture of a flower, whatever its shape, has only one basic purpose—production of fertile seed that will insure perpetuation of the species. This urgency toward reproduction is characteristic of all flowering plants. Typical of it is the profusion of pollen. The sperm cells, the male pollen, vastly outnumber the egg cells, the ovules.

I am struck by this prodigality of pollen each Spring when a big Norway spruce beside my house comes into flower. There are hundreds of catkinlike clusters of male flowers, but only a relatively few female flowers, or potential cones. When the pollen begins to fall it comes in a golden mist. We must at that time keep the windows closed on that side of the house or floors and furniture would be filmed with golden-tan spruce pollen. The floor of the porch is covered with it so thick that I sweep it into the windrows for the dustpan. All this from one big tree, and all waste pollen, pollen that failed to find a female ovule to fertilize. It is that one spruce tree's extravagant outpouring of male sperm to insure that perhaps one hundred cones shall be fertilized.

Every flowering plant does this, to some degree, from ragweed to columbine, from tulip to apple blossom. Wind-pollinated species, such as conifers and grasses, are most lavish with their pollen, but in all flowering plants there is an unbelievable prodigality of pollen production, a tremendous excess of male cells over female cells.

It is usually taken for granted that the petals of a flower were evolved to serve as landing platforms for the insects that pollinate it. This may be correct, but the reasoning is not necessarily absolute. It is also taken for granted that the petals are colored to attract insects. This too may be subject to challenge. Some researchers say that the insect eye cannot distinguish color. Others, with perhaps more persuasive evidence, insist that bees and certain other insects can see color, particularly in the red end of the spectrum.

When we speak of color we think of it in terms of our own vision. But color is a matter of wave length, and the human eye has a limited range of reception for such wave lengths. The color spectrum was devised as a gauge of man's visual range, but we now know that there are color waves beyond that rather limited range. It is conceivable that an insect eye—or the eye of a bird or an animal—could be unable to see color as we see it, and yet be capable of distinguishing color, even colors that we cannot see, in some other way. We know, from experiment, that at least some birds and some animals react to color visually much as human beings do. It is possible that through their eyes or even through some other organs they "hear" color or "smell" it, color of which the human eye is unaware. And it is possible that many of them are totally unaware of color.

When we say that a flower's petals are colored to attract insects, then, we are speculating on cause and effect. The color we see may be incidental to some emanation of which we are unaware. Or it may have still another purpose.

It is conceivable that the color of a flower has something to do with the plant's own vital need. We know, for instance that when a plant is germinating, flowering, or maturing seeds the plant's temperature is somewhat higher than at other times. Isn't it possible that a flower's petals trap heat or other forms of radiation, much as leaves trap energy from sunlight? I have noticed that many flowers that bloom in the shade have darker-colored petals than flowers of the same species that bloom in full sun. The jack-in-the-pulpit that blooms in deep shade has dark brownish-purple stripes on its green spathe, but the jack that blooms in full sun has faded or completely green stripes. I find the deeper-colored violets in the shade. And when I find wild anemones in bloom in April, those in the open are normally white but those in the shade are often flushed with pink. The same is true of bluets, those in the open usually white, those in the shade often tinged with lavender. I cannot see that this variation has anything to do with attracting pollinating insects.

I also see something of the same thing seasonally in wild flowers. In the Spring there is a preponderance of yellow. Yellow is toward the long-wave, or warm, end of the spectrum. In the Fall there is a preponderance of blues and purples, at the opposite end of the spectrum. And the same thing can be seen geographically. The warmer colors, the rich reds, oranges and yellows are typical of the tropics, while the blues and purples are typical of the temperate zones. The colors at the red end of the spectrum tend to reflect the long, hot waves of light, and the colors at the blue end tend to absorb those hot, infrared rays.

One can only speculate on the meaning of this. Perhaps someone someday will investigate it and learn some of the answers. It may be that the plant at its time of fertility, the time of flowering, needs extra heat and acquires it at least in part through the petals. The temperature in the female mammal rises at the time of fertility and the body provides it by slightly increased metabolism. Life has its mysterious parallels, plant and animal, in more surprising ways than this.

The variation of colors in a blossom is baffling, no matter what theory is used to explain them. For instance, where I live the wild Eastern columbine grows profusely. It is a beautiful wild flower, rich golden yellow and deep red. In the mountainous parts of Colorado where I once lived the wild columbine

102

grows also, a plant obviously from the same parent stock as the columbine of the East. But the Colorado columbine is usually blue and white instead of red and gold. Both flowers have substantially the same shape, though the sepals and petals of the Colorado variety are much larger than those of the Eastern native. Both are aided in pollination by the long-tongued moths and butterflies. Why did they evolve in such sharply divergent colors? One is at one end of the spectrum, the other at the opposite end. Can it be that the Colorado columbine needs to absorb more red heat rays of the sun to complete its seeding cycle? Does a mile's difference in altitude create such a divergence of color to meet some special need?

This whole matter of color in flowers is shot through with fascinating questions. But the blossom itself is really not at all mysterious. It is a rather complex arrangement of specialized organs designed to do a particular job—to produce male and female cells, to bring them together, and to create fertile seeds from which plants substantially like the parent will grow.

This is a process typical of all life. In one form or another it is found throughout both the plant and the animal kingdoms. I see it going on all around me each year, from the time the first coltsfoot comes to blossom in a sheltered hollow till the last aster fades and the witch hazel comes to bloom. I see it in the drift of "cotton" from the poplars and the blow of milkweed floss, in the pollen haze over the cornfields and the swarming of bees in the apple trees in May. I smell it when the lilacs bloom and the basswood drips its honey, when the clover whitens the meadow and when goldenrod makes September acrid.

It may be that the blossom is the highest achievement of the whole plant world. I find it fascinatingly complex. And it may be that members of the composite family—sunflowers, asters, goldenrods, thistles and all their kind—are the most advanced of all the flowering plants. I have already registered my reservations about that word "advanced." I would add only that to me the composite flowers, with their tightly packed heads of dozens of individual florets, have merely achieved a kind of community system, a "social organization" something like that of the ants. Perhaps this is advancement, of a kind. Perhaps it is an example of social efficiency. But each season I still celebrate the fact that there are the individuals, the wild lilies, the wild roses, the anemones, the columbines, who have thus far resisted such evolution. The flower is not only an efficient achievement; it is beautiful, and it is entitled to be as much of an individual as I am.

Trees

The Green Giants

THERE ARE many ways to define a tree, though I am not at all sure such a definition is necessary. To me, a tree is any large, woody-stemmed plant with a central stalk or bole. The botanists qualify this definition somewhat, but their meaning is essentially the same. Most people know a tree when they see one.

I happen to live in a timbered country, where trees are common, but by no means all parts of the earth are timbered. There are vast areas of America and of other continents where lesser plants thrive but trees are rare or entirely absent. Trees are rare on the Great Plains. They are dwarfed almost to the status of shrubs at high altitudes and in the polar zone. There are few trees in the deserts.

Because of their size, trees require a degree of soil fertility and a quantity of moisture beyond the needs of most lesser plants. Yet trees can not only survive but thrive on thin, stony soil—New England is proof of this. But the great forests occur in the deep-soiled, warm, wet areas. The greater part of North America, excepting the Great Plains and the Western deserts, once was one vast forest.

Trees as we know them came relatively late in the scale of living time. There were vast forests of big trees in the Carboniferous period, 300 million years ago, but they were largely tree ferns, alien and exotic to man and now known only in fossils. The early conifers, ancestors of my pines and hemlocks, did not appear in abundance until about 200 million years ago. And it was not until about 100 million years ago that recognizable ancestors of my modern maples, elms, hickories, sycamores, willows and birches were here. The flowering plants, including most of today's trees, were first numerous enough to leave a substantial fossil record in the Cretaceous period. That was the recognizable beginning of the forests of today. The Cretaceous period began about 120 million years ago.

The oldest living entities on this earth are the gigantic sequoia trees of California. Their kind dates back to the early beginnings of modern trees, and there are individual sequoias still growing that are at least five thousand years old. There are only two species of sequoia left, the Coastal Redwoods and the Big Trees of the Sierra Nevada. Both are gigantic, though the Big Trees are the larger, sometimes reaching 300 feet in height and twenty-four feet in trunk diameter. The two species are remnants from the age of the giant reptiles, the dinosaurian age, and perhaps they partook of whatever it was that urged both plants and animals of that remote age to tremendous bulk. But the giant lizards perished and the sequoias persisted.

All trees partake in some degree of that urgency toward bulk and size. Even the short-lived, relatively small gray birches in my own woodland are giants compared to the viburnums that grow in the rocky soil in the birch shade. And the gray birches are pygmies beside the sugar maples and the towering Norway spruce that grow here close to my house. Yet all are plants.

Botanists group plants in families according to similarities in essential elements of their physical structures, and a good many of these families include trees, shrubs and lesser flowering plants. The rose family, for instance, includes the apple trees in my pasture, the shad-blow that grows beside the river and the chokecherry on the hillside; it also includes the wild rose of my fence row, the wild strawberry, the cinquefoil, and the meadowsweet that lifts its pinkish plume in the meadow in late July. And the pulse family, in botanical terms, includes the garden peas we eat, the clover in my pasture, the vetch at the roadside, and the locust trees that cluster in a thorny tangle up on the mountainside.

In such terms, a tree is only a big plant with more woody fiber than its lesser cousins. But in a less restrictive sense a tree is a rather special living thing, an entity that has evolved its own means of building and fabricating woody fiber, cellulose, into a central trunk and branches, often of large height and diameter. That trunk is supported by an extensive root system that draws from the earth vast quantities of moisture and inorganic raw materials. On the branches it spreads a tremendous surface of chlorophyll in the form of leaves, to trap energy from sunlight and convert air and moisture into sugars and starches. And it has an extensive vascular system, a network of inner tubing and pumps, to lift water and sap from the lowest root to the highest twig, and to return from the canopy of leaves, at a proper time, the store of foodstuff needed to survive the Winter.

That is a tree. Add the means of creating fertile seeds, some sort of flowering mechanism, and you have the essentials of the forests and the shade that cools our homes and streets.

In terms of the big spans, it was the primitive trees that made possible the kind of life man knows today. There is no need here to speculate on whether primitive man originated in the

107

forests as an arboreal animal. No doubt the ancient forests provided shelter for primitive mammals, but man's particular phase of evolution is a little too misty to relate to the trees. The point I make here is that trees were the original substance of all the coal beds, and what we call civilization, the age of the machines, was built on the latent heat in coal, the stored carbon energy of those Paleozoic forests of trees. Man started on the path toward power-driven machines when he first found that coal would burn with more intense and more enduring heat than a billet of wood.

But all along the way toward the power age, man was sheltered and comforted by the trees. Whether he went from the trees to the caves or not, back at his beginnings, he eventually went from the caves to the woodland. Trees provided him with roof and walls. They gave him his first raft, his first boat, eventually the ships in which he roamed the rivers and shallow seas. The tree provided his weapons, the club, the lance, the bow, the arrow. Its resins and other juices gave him medicines and glue and crude chemicals. Sap provided syrup, nuts provided oil, the flesh of fruit fed him. Bark clothed him and gave him cordage. Man was never in dire need as long as he intimately knew the forests. And when he deserted the woods, they still gave him the substance with which to build his villages and towns and cities.

The most primitive of all existing trees are the cycads, of which the best known of America's four species is the sago palm.

The ginkgo tree, native now only to China but grown as an ornamental tree in American cities, is possibly older in its origins than the sago palm, but it probably has changed more in structure than the cycads, over the eons since its beginning.

Next after the cycads and the ginkgo came the conifers—the pines and all their kind. Among the oldest of them are the sequoia, but the pines, the firs, the hemlocks, the spruces and all the rest of them came not long after, and they inherited the cooler regions of this earth. Only one among them, the tamarack, adopted the deciduous habit of shedding its leaves each Autumn. The others cling to their leaves the year around. But all conifer leaves have been reduced to—or never advanced beyond—the familiar needle shape. The very earliest trees had scalelike leaves, something like the scale leaves on today's cedars, and apparently these were adapted into such leaves as the long, thin needles on my white pines, slim but efficient and tough enough to face Winter cold in most climates.

After the conifers probably came those trees that bear catkins, though the postconifer sequence is not certain. The willows, the poplars, and the birches are among the catkin-bearers. Sometimes the catkins are bisexual, having both male and female organs. Sometimes they are unisexual, producing either pollen or seeds but not both. In some species, there are trees that bear only male catkins and other trees that bear only female catkins.

The similarity of the catkin to the cone is not too obscure. I see it most pronounced in the alder bushes that grow in the lowlands, for the alder's seed catkin, the female, looks much like the small hemlock cone when it is ripe with seed.

After the first catkin-bearers, though the span may have been relatively brief, came most of the fruiting trees, those with true blossoms. Among them are the maples, the oaks, the hickories, the lindens, the whole rose family of apples and peaches and plums and cherries. Most of the true flowering trees were in existence about 100 million years ago; virtually all of them were here by the beginning of the Tertiary period about sixty million years ago. These dates are significant primarily in relation to man. The earliest date given for primitive man's appearance is only about one million years ago, and that may be a generous estimate.

Forests essentially the same as those man has always known were here when the great ice ages came. It is a tribute to the tenacity of the conifers that they persisted through those cold centuries, for the ice sheets sheared off millions of them in the

glacial advances from the north. The conifers have always pre-
ferred the colder regions of the earth, so they were the first
trees in the path of the advancing ice. But somehow the conifers
did persist, and so did all the other trees we know today. They
learned to grow in an altered climate, and each time the ice
retreated the trees enlarged their range again. Life, all life,
both plant and animal, ebbs and flows with the conditions and
even plant life moves from place to place. Slow growth and lack
of legs with which to run may impede the movement of trees,
but they migrate just the same. I have but to look at the constant
encroachment of brush and trees on any abandoned field or
pasture to know the persistent truth of this.

When, at last, the great ice sheets retreated north and did not
return, the trees followed the ice northward. They had new land
to conquer, a wholly different aspect of hill and valley. Most of
the ice-scarred land was stripped of topsoil. The New England
where I live was a desolate place, a landscape of shorn rock and
vast heaps of glacial debris, threaded by rushing streams carrying silt-laden ice melt down to the oceans.

The scars of those times remain today here on my own acres.
Perhaps twenty thousand years of insistent, benevolent growth
have clothed the rocks somewhat with soil, and the valleys are
silted in many places and rich with plant-grown loam. But the
topsoil is thin. In geological terms, there has been little time
for the trees to mellow the land. My own valley is filled with silt
and that silt has an overlying layer of natural humus. That is
what gives it its fertility. But if I dig only a foot or so into this
valley soil I come to sand with only the slightest trace of humus.
In all those centuries, the trees and lesser plants have laid down
only a few inches of organic matter over the sands that date back
to the ice ages.

Man went through a strange series of relationships with the
trees. They sheltered him for a long time. Then he quit the

forests, and the woods became a place of dark mystery and fearful unknowns. Awesome beasts, real and legendary, lived in the
forests, and savage men and outlaws lived there. The old tales
and the venerable legends are full of the terrors of the unknown
woods. The ancient civilizations were constantly menaced by the
barbarians from the forests. Civilization came to mean a conquest over the trees, a beating back of the woods with their
terrors and their menaces. Northern Europe was a land of deep
woods and dour savages, and civilization centered on the Mediterranean shores where the trees had been conquered.

But in the woodland there were people who had learned to
live with the trees, who had made a truce with the forests. It was
an uneasy truce in many ways, and it demanded of the forest
dwellers an often elaborate ritual. There were gods of the trees,
and demons of the trees, and these gods and demons had to be
appeased. Among the best known of these people's rites were
those of the Druids, to whom all plant life was in some measure
sacred, with the oak tree most sanctified of all. Druidic rites
were common in Gaul and in Britain, throughout the area dominated by the Celts. The Druids were so powerful in those areas
that when the Romans sought to rule there they had to forbid
all Druidical practices. Even then, for many years they failed
to put an end to Druidism. A whole body of law and religion
as well as an elaborate ritual was built around the beliefs of the
Druids. A civilization of no mean stature evolved from Druidism, though it eventually was overwhelmed by the Romans and
displaced by the culture evolved on those tree-tamed Mediterranean shores.

When the first white men came to America they found a land
of trees. Old records show that the Hudson Valley when Henry
Hudson first saw it was one vast stand of towering white pines.
All the early settlements of New England were hemmed close
to the shore by the forests, dark and forbidding. By that time,

111

much of England and western Europe was an old land with few primitive forests. But the legends persisted. Deep woods were full of terrors and danger.

The conquest of America was accompanied and even paced by the rhythm of the ax. For years the skies of the near frontier were darkened by the smoke from burning trees. At the very best, the trees were a nuisance to the farmer. He cut them and he burned them, that he might plow the land. Wood, for lumber or for fuel, was anyone's for the taking, and the game of the forests was a community larder. But the forests had to go before the settlers could possess the land. Only the fugitive and the frontiersman, the leather-clad hunter and trapper, ever made peace with the trees.

Old records in my community show how, in 1738, a handful of settlers made their way, in some peril, from Hartford west to this valley to establish a settlement. They had to hew a track through the woods for their laden carts, and it took them several weeks to make a trip that I now can make in an hour. These New England woodlands had no roads, not even any pathways except the game trails and a few Indian trails that might serve a man on horseback. That was one reason the rivers were the first highways. On the river one did not have to clear the way, cut the trees and then bump over the stumps.

The forests dictated the early pattern of settlement, not only here but all over the world. The first farmers lived in villages, and those villages were in natural clearings beside the streams. They only slowly and cautiously extended their farmlands, wresting them acre by acre from the forests. And when the farmer finally cleared a field beyond sight of the village and went there to live, he was a man of courage and of remarkable independence. But he set his house in the midst of a clearing, and he extended that clearing as swiftly as ax and fire could do it. He seldom regarded the forest as anything but his enemy.

I can remember my own grandfather saying, the first time he saw the Great Plains with their horizon-wide treelessness, "A man can plow a furrow here a mile long and never have to go around a tree or a stump." He said it in awe. He had spent all his life till then in timbered country, fighting trees and stumps. And he spent that life in Missouri and Nebraska, 1,600 miles from the Atlantic Coast. In my great-grandfather's day there had been an almost unbroken forest all that distance, interrupted only by a scattering of farms and towns carved out of the wood-land.

It is difficult today to understand this warfare between man and trees, yet in essence it has been nothing more than an example of the eternal competition among living things for living space. As long as man remained a primitive creature he could dwell in relative peace with the trees, occupying a kind of niche in the habitat, which is nature's lot for most animals. But when man began to multiply and to insist on more living space, when he tamed grasses and created field crops, the nearest woodlands became his enemy. There could be a truce with the trees only when man had asserted his dominance over whatever land he needed. He was no longer content with a niche in the forest. And as mankind proliferated and his way of life became more and more complex, the very simplicity and the basic insistence of the trees had to be brought under man's control. Whatever truce was reached must be on man's terms.

Today we cherish our woodlands. The virgin forest has become a rarity, and we have set aside almost 200 million acres of state and national forests as reservations. There are those who say that we pillaged our woodlands in the great days of lumbering. But the trees cut at that time had their useful destiny. If there was pillage, it was much earlier, when millions of acres of primitive forests were cut and burned to make way for the farms. That timber went up in smoke and served no useful purpose. Yet even that was a conquest of the land, which in its time was a personal and a national necessity. One cannot be too glib about such matters, or too indignant.

I look about me here and wonder what this land, this particular valley, looked like two hundred years ago, or even one hundred years ago. The whole mountainside behind my house is timbered, grown up with white pine, hemlock, oak, maple and ash, with a scattering of birch and other lesser trees. Of my own land, only a relatively narrow strip along the river is cleared and in use as pastureland. Two hundred years ago, as the records run, this whole valley was wooded, but undoubtedly there was a clear strip along the river, perhaps a line of meadows not much different from those I see today. The lowland here was an old flood plain. The timber was big timber, of course, oaks and chestnuts perhaps a hundred feet tall and big as a barrel in girth. It had been here since time forgotten. And there were white pines bigger than the towering Norway spruce in my dooryard. But the Indians who lived here and hunted here and grew corn on the flatlands of the valley occasionally set fires that roared through the underbrush, driving game before it. Occasionally they set such fires to drive that game into the river, where they could kill a whole Winter's meat in an hour's work with a knife.

A hundred years ago much of my mountainside was laid out in fields and cultivated. It is timbered today, but when I walk through those woods I find a crisscrossing of stone walls, and the farmers never hauled such stones from the valley to build those walls; they moved those stones from the fields themselves, to clear the way for the plow. In some of those walls are trees two feet through at the butt. They grew there since those fields were abandoned.

A neighbor tells me that when he was a boy, and that was only forty years ago, there was a large hayfield on that mountainside, tended and mowed each Summer. Today that old hayfield is a tangle of white pine and gray birch, pine big enough for saw

logs. There isn't a trace of a furrow there, and there are stumps
of chestnut trees two feet through which were cut for lumber
for my house. Perhaps the chestnuts stood in the hayfield, but the
pines didn't. They have grown up during my neighbor's lifetime.

Man's truce with the trees on my mountainside was kept only
so long as the farmers lived to enforce it. But those men were
mortal. They lived and worked and died. And the trees crept
silently back. They kept no truce. It is their way of life to possess
the land, and there is something that we call patience in a
tree. It can wait. It can live two hundred years, waiting, sowing
its seed each season. Eventually some of those seeds will find
soil that nourishes, and they will find man with his back turned.
The truce will be broken without a sound louder than the fall
of an acorn. Thus the trees creep back over the land.

A tree is a noble thing, a tribute to the spark of life and its
persistence. If I cut a fence post from a willow tree and put it in
the ground, it grows. It becomes another tree. I can cut the gray
birch at the edge of the pasture every year of my life, and when
I am gone there will still be gray birches growing there. If I were
to cut and burn every sugar maple along my road, in ten years
there would be a new grove of maples there, for the seedlings
are there in the grass right now.

I live in a house built of lumber cut on my own mountainside.
Yet that mountainside is still a timbered place. The old stumps
are all surrounded by middle-aged trees, self-sown. Even in the
dry grassland of the Great Plains where I grew up there were an
occasional cottonwood and a few stunted willows in the valleys
where water flowed from time to time. Now and then a cottonwood was felled by lightning, but always there were new seedlings to take its place, and at least one of them always seemed to
survive.

The first tree grew out of the primeval muck at least 300
million years ago, a new adventure in plant life. Animals came

and went. Species vanished. Man eventually appeared. And
the trees persisted. Without arms or legs or brains or eyes or
ears, they still persist. And richly endowed man still has
achieved no victory over the tree. The best he has been able to
do is arrive at an armistice with the forest, an uneasy truce that
will end two minutes after man goes away.

Parasites

Battle for Existence

WE USUALLY THINK of plant life as peaceful existence, properly removed from the bitterness of competition and the violence of war and murder to which the other living kingdom, the flesh-and-blood kingdom of animals, is prone. The meadowful of daisies, the woodland of oaks and maples and pines, even the bogland of cattails and skunk cabbage and purple-headed ironweed, seem ideally arranged in a quiet pattern of peaceful coexistence. But the truth is not quite so idyllic. The battle for existence, the struggle for living space and livelihood, goes on in the plant kingdom just as ruthlessly, if not so noisily, as it does elsewhere. And the winners thrive and proliferate, the losers fade and vanish. There are no idealists in the plant world, and there is no compassion. The rose and the morning glory know no mercy. Idealism and mercy are human terms and nature doesn't seem to be concerned with them in the slightest.

Plant competition, like animal competition, is for the necessities of life. Plants need water, air, sunlight and root space. And it is not always the vigorous plant giant that wins the battle. Trees can starve grass to death, but a vine that unassisted cannot lift its leaves a foot off the ground can choke a tree to death. In the corner of my study stands a length of white birch that is gnarled and twisted and grooved. I cut it from a dead tree twenty feet tall. That tree had the misfortune, in its sapling days, to have a bittersweet vine grow close beside it. The vine, reaching for support, touched the young birch, twined around it and began to climb. As the vine spiraled upward, lifting its leaves toward the sun, it clasped the sapling in its coils. As the tree grew it ridged itself against the clasp of the vine, grew into the shape dictated by its embracing guest. Eventually the birch died, not hugged to death but robbed of sunlight and in some way weakened so that it could not survive. When I found it, the tree was dead and the vine was thriving.

Woodbine can do the same thing. Each Fall I watch the flame of woodbine leaves across the river, a tower of crimson on the dead trunk of a poplar tree that was weakened and died. Perhaps it would have died without the presence of the vine, but there is the presumption that the vine hastened its death. Wild grapes can do the same thing, and so can poison ivy. And all without a cry or a visible struggle.

On the High Plains of my boyhood there were areas where yucca, the Spanish bayonet, grew profusely. Yet the yucca plants were seldom massed in a spiny tangle; they usually grew as individual plants some distance apart. I often wondered why they were so evenly spaced. Later I knew that it was because that land of little rain provided only so much moisture, and the spacing of the yuccas was dictated, at least in part, by their water needs. It was also a result of a toxic agent that many desert plants produce to inhibit the sprouting of competitors for scarce water.

If I were to leave my own patch of bluegrass lawn to the natural struggle of the plants, in a very few years the grass would be gone and in its place would be dandelions, plantain and chickweed, which are forever trying to get the upper hand. The grass wins only because of my assistance, which is human interference in the natural warfare of the plants. And without my interference with hoe and cultivator, my vegetable garden would be the scene of war to death among quack grass, pigweed, purslane and German weed. Even my vigorous asparagus and my rhubarb need my help to maintain anything approaching dominance in their small areas.

It is a fundamental struggle, as old as life itself, and it is exemplified in every cultivated field and tended woodland. Man chooses the plants, whether they are forage crops or grain or trees, that he wishes to assist, and he gives them all the help he can. It has been thus ever since the first farmer sowed a handful of wild rye seeds.

But this constant competition, this war between the plants marked by the green of chlorophyll, is even less important in the plant world than the war between all green, self-supporting plants and the parasitic plants that have no chlorophyll. The fungi, a breed of plant life that learned many millions of years ago to live on the labors of others, is a constant, inconspicuous threat to everything green upon this earth. And it is a threat that is not diminishing. Today there is at least one fungus species for every three species of flowering plants that work for a living. The fungi make others do the work of gathering food. They live on organic matter, and their choice hosts are green plants.

The fungi spread by means of spores, one of the most venerable of all means of reproduction. Each spore is a single cell en-

119

dowed with an intense urge to grow. Most of these fungus spores
are invisible, too small to be seen by the naked eye. They ride
the breeze, millions of them, and they are constantly falling on
the leaves and the stems of green plants. Most of the spores find
no lodging place and soon lose their spark of life. But the fungi
produce vast numbers of spores. By the law of averages, they
persist and even multiply. Of what consequence is the loss of
a million spores if one finds a place to live, grow and produce
two million new spores?

A spore lodged on a green plant sometimes finds an opening
through which it can make its way into the living plant tissue.
All plant stems and all leaves have minute pores through which
they breathe. If a spore finds such a pore and worms its way inside, the fungus has a foothold. As soon as the spore gets inside,
in contact with living plant tissue, it begins to grow. It grows
into a mycelium, a kind of minute mass of filaments that reaches
out in all directions. The mycelium fibers thrust their way between the cells of the plant and occasionally burst the cell walls.
Once inside a cell, the fiber of this parasitic intruder begins to
feed on the protoplasm. The parasite, the plant grown from
that fungus spore, has tapped a source of food and energy. All it
has to do is feed and grow. So it grows, extends its filaments to
other cells, begins to take over the food and substance of the
hard-working host plant.

One such parasitic fungus can starve a healthy plant to death.
It can eat out the substance of the plant's leaves or choke the
plant's stem. It can destroy the host plant's flowers and make
seeding impossible. But—and this is a grim truth that merely
points up the insidious cycle—the invading fungus usually does
not kill its host until the fungus itself has matured to the point
where it is ready to produce spores. It comes to its own ripeness,
scatters its millions of spores, which seek other green plants, and
then it usually proceeds to finish the murder of the host, for
which it no longer has any need.

Man is most aware of these fungi when they attack plants he wants or needs. Smut that attacks corn is such a fungus. On corn this fungus attacks only the maturing kernels on the ear, but it does widespread damage. The rusts are another destructive fungus, and one of their principal targets is the cereal grains.

There are about a thousand species of rust fungi in the United States alone. They are distantly related to the mushrooms, though the rusts are largely microscopic and the mushrooms are often of considerable size. Some of the most destructive rusts pass through two stages, one of which requires a host plant quite different from that on which it does the most damage. Stem rust, for instance, which is particularly injurious to wheat, passes its intermediate stage in the wild barberry, where it forms yellowish patches on the leaves. These patches produce spores that attack wheat. By getting rid of barberry bushes near wheat or barley or rye fields, much of the stem rust damage has been stopped. Other forms of rust use the wild currant as an intermediate host. In my area all the wild-currant bushes have been cleaned out, not because they are themselves a pest but because they harbor the form of rust that produces spores that attack cereal grains.

The smuts are particularly insidious because the spores invade the grain itself. A single grain of wheat, for example, may carry 200,000 smut spores. These spores can survive several seasons, latent in the soil, so one crop of smut-infested seed can infect a field for years.

The chestnut blight that has killed virtually all the chestnut trees in America is a form of fungus. Its spores invade the trees through wounds in the bark and spread their hungry mycelium as a fibrous, cottony mass. If it starts on the trunk of the tree, it eventually girdles the tree, destroys the cambium tissue through which sap and food are circulated, and the tree dies. If the attack is on a branch, the branch is killed and the fungus continues to spread.

The Dutch elm disease, which has attacked New England's

elms over the past quarter century, is a similar fungus disease. It acts in much the same way, eventually choking the tree to death.

Not all the invading fungi are so ruthless. Some of them merely form galls or tumors, knobby growths on a plant or a tree, or even on a leaf, where the fungi live and draw sustenance from the host plant but do not proceed with outright murder. Perhaps one could liken them to nonmalignant tumors in the human body, whereas the smuts and rusts and the chestnut and elm diseases could be likened to cancer.

There are still other fungi that live with hosts and contribute an essential element to the host's life. The lichens, for instance, are dual entities, consisting of algae and fungi living in a co-operative kind of agreement in situations where neither one could live alone. This mutual dependence is called symbiosis, from the Greek words for "living together."

Lichens live on rocks where few or no other plants can survive. In their symbiosis, the algae provide the food and the fungi store the necessary water and secrete acids which eat into the rocks and assure the symbiotic plant a foothold. The algae have chlorophyll, use air and moisture to manufacture food. The fungi are colorless, manufacture no food, and are wholly dependent on the algae for sustenance. Together they make out very well. Other forms of this symbiotic life of algae and fungi are reindeer moss and the trailing pale-green streamers of old-man's-beard on spruce and fir trees of the north.

The largest of the fungi, these plants that are unable to manufacture their own food, are the mushrooms. They, too, need organic matter to live on, but many of them live on dead vegetable matter and only a relatively few invade living trees. Most of the mushrooms are scavengers rather than parasites, for they live on the remains of living things, not on living things themselves.

Those of us who live in wooded areas have but to step into the woodland to find some form of mushrooms. Dead wood is the chosen food for many of them. They are common on old stumps and fallen trees, and if one finds a damp, well-shaded spot in the woods with a litter of rotting wood, one is sure to find mushrooms. They cannot live long in sunlight, for the heat withers them. They are plentiful in many meadows after a rainy spell, and I find the edible morels in my dooryard after a few days of rain and dampness in any May. Within twelve hours after the rain stops, however, and the sun strikes them full force, they shrivel and die.

There are more than 200 species of wild mushrooms, and in this group are found a good many poisonous ones. And mushroom poisoning is not to be laughed at. At the least, it causes painful intestinal upset and nausea. At the worst, it causes death. The deadly amanitas are among the most poisonous of all plants and are especially dangerous because the poison has already done its major damage before the symptoms of poisoning appear.

On living trees as well as dead ones there are the bracket fungi, many of them looking like oyster shells, some of them more than a foot across. These "brackets" are the outward indication of what is happening inside the tree. If it happens to be a dead tree, the fungus is merely eating away the lifeless but still organic wood. If the tree is still alive, the fungus is slowly eating into it and spreading its mycelium, which will eventually weaken and kill that tree.

All these forms of fungal life spread themselves and propagate new fungi by means of spores. Just how old they are, in the long history of life, nobody knows. They are probably very old, but there are few evidences of such insubstantial plants in the fossil records.

They are important not only economically—in man's terms as well as in nature's—but probably in terms of evolution. The parasitic fungi, which are in the vast majority, learned long ago the same basic habit that dominates all animal life. Fungi eat food which some other form of life manufactured.

In human terms, this may not be a pretty picture. But nature has no knowledge of such terms, no awareness of or respect for them. Nature is life, and life makes its own way with no sense of morality. Man, when he is tempted to draw judgments in these matters, might well remember that he is essentially an animal and should reserve such judgment for his own kind. He, too, lives on other living things. Without the chlorophyll in the growing leaf, man would perish. It happens that man eats not only the chlorophyll-manufactured sugars and starches but the flesh of other animals that live on the same thing. Man is, by strict definition, a parasite, and he would be wise to temper his judgment of other parasites.

This ability to live on the labor of other plants is typical of the fungi. How they learned it, or evolved it, is unknown. But they have this attribute, this ability, in common with animals. And when one follows the biological trail only a little further one comes to strange, perverse organisms that are almost impossible to classify as plant or animal. There are water-dwelling animals that look and act like plants. There is a green alga that swims about like an animal and yet is a plant. And there are the slime molds which are typical of neither plants nor animals yet are close relatives, as such relationships go, of the fungi.

Slime molds have no chlorophyll and are unable to manufacture their own food. Yet they are not, strictly speaking, parasites. They live on decaying vegetable matter, chiefly on rotting wood. And slime mold has no clearly defined physical form, as does a mushroom or even the mycelium of wheat rust or the parasitic chestnut blight. Slime mold consists of a mass of naked protoplasm, the basic substance of all living cells. But this slime mold's protoplasm has no confining cell walls and no specialized organs of any kind. It is gray or yellowish in color and it has the consistency of the albumen of an egg. From time to time I pick up a piece of rotting log in a damp part of my woods and feel the slime mold, greasy and unpleasant under my fingers.

This formless slime mold spreads slowly over whatever it touches. It seems almost to flow, and it does have a capacity for movement. As it goes, it sucks in, or at least surrounds and absorbs, whatever it finds in the way of organic food, bits of wood, bacteria, anything that is edible to slime mold. It absorbs this food and flows on, digesting what it can use and leaving waste material behind. It has no entity except this greasy, formless being, this slimy coating that is the total of slime mold. But now and then it thrusts up from its surface small warts or knobs which grow into spore cases. The spores ripen and drift away on the wind, and if they find a suitable piece of damp, rotting wood they flow toward similar spores and create a new patch of slime mold, another naked film of protoplasmic jelly, a new generation.

So there is the slime mold, technically a plant yet endowed with movement and having other animal characteristics. Its spores even have flagella, microscopic hairs which enable them to move about when they have been wind-borne to a suitable place for growth. There near the very bottom of the vast heap of life patterns, endowed with what seem to be the very minimum of equipment for successful living, they persist and have no doubt persisted for millions of years. In terms of persisting life, which is the fundamental gauge, they are successful. Somehow even they have survived the eternal war. And they have a purpose, as far as we can evaluate purpose, for they are scavengers of a kind; they help to reduce dead plant life to a form that can be used over again by other plants, self-supporting plants.

It is difficult, if not impossible, to assess value for any form of life. Man persists in evaluating, and nearly always in terms of his own wants and needs. But nature has a quite different scale of values of which I am not at all sure we are aware except in its most general outlines. Life seems to be a purpose in itself, the fact of living and growing and perpetuating. Perhaps there is also the purpose of perfection, though I am wary of that term. Perfection in this sense would have to mean maximum possible development of a life form in a particular environment.

If one agrees with that, then the competition among life forms becomes inevitable, and even on this limited, natural basis man has a responsibility to his own kind—to his own peculiar form of life. For some reason, man is endowed with intelligence and with ethical and moral values. It is his responsibility to use them to the utmost. He came along at a propitious time in the history of life on earth and he filled a niche that was unoccupied. There must have been a purpose for him, since nature seems to be organized on what man calls a purposive plan. This statement, of course, is made by a man, who again is drawing his own humanly biased conclusions.

But here is this world of life, teeming with different forms, plant and animal and forms not easily distinguishable as either. Here is this green world, this plant world, which seems at a glance to be so peaceful, so well ordered, so quiet and self-contained. And beneath that calm surface is this constant and unremitting struggle, this competition which makes less noise than the fall of a leaf. The balance in that world is so precarious that the shift of an ocean current or a prevailing wind can upset it. A cold air mass moves a hundred miles south and settles down there for a few weeks, and whole states are swept with snow, crops are frozen, man's own economics are upset.

Animal life is somewhat less at the mercy of such changes. Animals can move about, migrate to more favorable climate. Yet the whole animal population of the world is at the mercy of the rooted, green-leafed plants that cannot readily move. A changing climate can displace even the insect life of an area. And since insects often carry bacteria, the displacement of a

126

swarm of mosquitoes could conceivably change the whole plant and animal life of a considerable area. For a time. Eventually a new balance would be struck, a new truce of sorts, and plants and animals would assume their proper places. This has happened countless times in the past, and there is no reason to believe it will never happen again.

The war goes on. It has been going on for many millions of years. Out of it have come adaptations of old species to new conditions and the evolution of new species. Somewhere in the vast storehouse of nature there seems always to be a strain of life that is ready to creep into any opening, to occupy it, to grow, to proliferate, to fill the vacuum. If there is any inevitability in nature as we know it, it is life itself, growth and change. But the basis of it all, today at least, is the green world, the leaf with its chlorophyll and its ability to manufacture food. Every other form of life depends on the green leaf, even those forms of life which are constantly at war with it.

Life—
The Pygmy Hordes

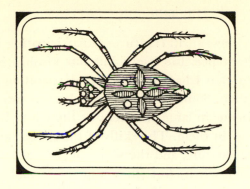

Spiders

Eight Legs and a Silken Strand

THE WORLD I KNOW is more densely populated by insects
and other small exoskeletal creatures—animals with their
entire skeleton outside rather than inside the body—than by
any other form of visible animal life. Some naturalists put the
number of insect species at more than 600,000, ten or fifteen
times the number of known species of fish, amphibians, reptiles, birds and mammals combined; others put the number
still higher, around 750,000. The total number of insects, of all
species, is beyond even rough estimate. Here on my own small
farm, for instance, I am sure there are many millions of ants,
though ants are not a pest to us. And besides ants there are
beetles, bees, wasps, spiders and all the others. I wouldn't try
to guess at the number of them even in the vegetable garden,
which is but a fraction of one acre.

I recognize these small creatures as participating in the great common inheritance, life itself; but our kinship is so remote and so strange that I have difficulty understanding even its occasional parallels. Some of these parallels even rouse a kind of resentment in me, in large part because there is so little of what I call "feeling" in them. The skills of the spider, an ant, a bee or a wasp are amazing, and the social organization of bees and ants is grimly efficient; but their kind of mental activity and their range of emotions, if they are really emotions and not mere reflexes, are so wholly different from mine and those of the other animals I know that we live in almost completely different worlds.

Yet we share this earth, those other creatures and my own kind, and we share this common heritage, life. We are, both of us, breathers of air, we eat and digest food, we multiply, and our kinds persist. We belong to the same brotherhood of living things.

But the spiders and the insects, in their line of evolution, went one way, and my kind went another. They long ago perfected a way of life concentrated on one object alone, perpetuation of the species. Apparently they did this by perfecting certain instincts and suppressing others. And somehow their brains never developed far beyond the capacity needed for survival. Long ago they learned the necessary techniques of their kind of life, and they never advanced beyond that.

My kind seems never to have been content with mere perpetuation. Man's brain developed beyond the simple requirements of survival. Beyond instinct, man has a power of memory and anticipation. And, for some reason that I applaud but do not even attempt to explain, man evolved emotions, the capacity for joy, grief, pleasure, pain and compassion. He achieved an intellect, the ability to think in abstractions, to imagine, to create both things and ideas. Man reached for understanding, not only of himself but of everything around him. In that sense, man is unique.

I shall speak later of the insects, particularly the social insects, but here I shall go back still further and speak of the Arachnida, a Greek term meaning spiderlike creatures. I choose this order only because the spiders and their kinfolk are even older than the amphibians. Fossil evidence indicates that they were here close to a million years before the first backboned creature crawled out onto the land and learned to live at least a part of its life out of the water. The oldest fossils of spiders, scorpions and harvestmen, or daddy longlegs, date back approximately 300 million years. Fossil bees and ants date back only about 150 million years.

Scientists make clear distinctions between insects and members of the spider family. An insect is an air-breathing animal with three body parts, head, thorax and abdomen, one pair of antennae, and six legs. A spider is also an air-breathing creature, but it has only two body parts, a cephalothorax and an abdomen, it has no antennae, and it has eight legs.

Nobody knows precisely what was the origin of either insects or the spider family. The supposition is that they diverged, many millions of years ago, from some early form of aquatic life. Theories about their beginnings reach back to various forms of shellfish, most of them small and most of them having a larval stage in their development. There is speculation that insect wings evolved from external gills in a very early ancestor, but nobody knows.

There is one strong clue to the origin of the spider family. That is the creature we know as the king or horseshoe crab. It is not a crab. It is an arachnoid, closely related to the scorpion, and it is a kind of living fossil. It exists today in almost exactly the same form it existed, by fossil evidence, close to 200 million years ago. There is strong evidence that it was at least one of the links between the marine creatures and the whole spider family. But where the change came, and when and how, are enduring mysteries.

To the experts it may be a dubious clue, but to me there is a strange coincidence in the fact that spiders, insects and crustaceans all have shells or external skeletons composed of the same substance—chitin. And chitin occurs nowhere else in nature except, of all places, in a member of the plant world, a certain fungus. Chitin is an amorphous, horny substance that looks and feels something like my own fingernails. Chemically, it is not like either my fingernails or any animal's horns. It is simply chitin, a tough substance chemically composed of carbon, hydrogen, nitrogen and oxygen. It forms the claws of lobsters that I crack to reach the meat inside. It protects the body of the crawfish in my river. It is the substance of a shrimp's papery shell. It is the beetle's many-colored shell. It is even the fragile outer skeleton of the fly, the mosquito—and the spider.

The bodily structure of a spider is remarkable. It is so efficient, so near perfection for its purpose, that one must admire it. It is also so complex and so fully equipped with specialized organs that one would think it was the result of long evolution. Yet the earliest of fossil spiders and scorpions show substantially the same perfection of organization that we find in living spiders and scorpions today.

The spider has eight eyes situated in the upper front of its head. It has a pair of palps on the under surface of the head, a kind of combination of fingers and jaws. It has a lung with sheets of lung tissue like pages in a book; they open and close as air is drawn in through an opening in the abdomen. It has a heart which circulates very pale blue blood, almost colorless; its faint color comes from copper in the blood rather than the iron which makes my own blood red. It has glands called spinnerets through which a liquid is secreted to form the familiar spider silk. And any one of the eight legs, each seven-jointed, can be sacrificed without injury to the spider. The lobster, too, can sacrifice a leg without injury, and like the spider the lobster will eventually grow a new leg or a new joint of a leg to replace the lost one.

Spiders come in all sizes, from that of a pinhead to that of a dinner plate. And, despite their seeming awkwardness, spiders are swift on their feet. They can run, comparative size considered, about five times as fast as a human sprinter. They have an acute sense of touch, apparently in the hairs on their body and in the palps on the head. No one knows whether they can hear or not, but it is supposed that they feel sound vibrations through the body hairs, and thus have the equivalent of a sense of hearing. Some spiders can make sounds. They probably have a sense of smell. And they definitely have a sense of taste.

The spider's brain is not much more than a nerve center and there seems little doubt that no spider has more than a glimmering of intelligence. Kept in captivity, spiders will learn to come toward the person who feeds them, but this appears to be only a conditioned reflex. It would indicate some degree of memory, perhaps, but it is no proof at all of rational intelligence. There is no such proof, so the conclusion is that spiders do not think.

Briefly, then, a spider (or a scorpion, or a daddy longlegs, or a tick—they all belong to the same family) is a complex form of life, ideally equipped for survival but so remote from my form of life that it seems almost entirely alien. Yet men have been in awe of spiders for generations, and men still admire them for their accomplishments.

The spider's accomplishments are quite remarkable, but I wonder at the use of that word "accomplishments." An accomplishment, to me, implies conscious purpose and a degree of planning. That comes close to intelligence. So suppose I amend the statement. I shall say that a spider can do remarkable things. I am convinced that most of those things are done by instinct, because young spiders as well as old ones can do them and there is no training of the young by their parents.

A spider, for instance, can spin a silken line one 250 thousandth of an inch in diameter. Such a line is stronger than a steel wire of the same diameter. Baby spiders, fresh from the cocoon, spin such lines a few feet long, use them as parachutes, and ride the breeze for surprising distances. Spiders so borne by the air have been found five miles above the earth, and they have been found two hundred miles at sea. That apparently is the way they have traveled all over the earth, for they are found not only in the tropics and the temperate zones but well inside the Arctic Circle and 22,000 feet up on Mount Everest.

The spider uses this silk in many different ways. It makes webs in which to trap insects for food. It makes trap doors of silk to protect its nests. It weaves cocoons in which its eggs are protected until they hatch. It weaves waterproof cages in which it can live under water.

The orb spiders, those which weave the beautiful webs that deck the weeds and grass near my house and seem to be studded with pearls on a misty morning, have long been credited with well-developed mathematical skills. Actually, even the best orb-spider web is a rather haphazard piece of construction, mathematically speaking. The foundation lines form a quadrangle, usually, but they are never a perfect square or even a perfect parallelogram. And the crosslines, the spokes or radii, never have equal angles at the center. No spider has yet qualified as a mathematician, or even as an elementary geometrician. Instinct tells them to make webs and how, in a rather specific way, to build them. But that instinct does not know how to count or how to measure an angle. And the orb spiders are the only ones whose instinct tells them to make a superficially symmetrical web. The webs of most other spiders are random masses of silk, more like a tangle of thread than a designed structure.

Spiders have no social instinct. They do not even live or travel in pairs. Their mating processes are peculiar, almost unique. The male spider excretes his seminal fluid, takes it up in one of his palps, and seeks a female. Sometimes he performs a kind of courtship dance, but on other occasions he approaches the prospective mate with stealth. There is no evidence of anything approaching affection between them. The male impregnates the female with his sperm-laden palp. And sometimes, but not always, the female thereupon kills and eats the male. In any case, there is no further association between the male and the female.

After mating, the female spins silk and shapes a cocoon in which she lays her eggs. The number may vary from a few to several hundred. The black widow spider sometimes lays only twenty-five at a time, and she sometimes stuffs a cocoon with as many as nine hundred; and the black widow may produce nine cocoons of eggs in a season. Spiders make sure that they leave a new generation behind them.

The eggs hatch in a week or so—black-widow eggs take from ten to fourteen days. In most species the hatchlings remain in the cocoon at least a week, sometimes six weeks, eating leftover food from the eggs from which they were hatched. Then they leave the cocoon, miniature spiders but already equipped with a full set of instincts and organs, everything they need for adult spider life except sex glands. They begin to grow and molt, shedding their constricting chitin skin from time to time and growing a new one. Black-widow males are sexually mature after five molts, females after seven or eight. But before the second molt most spiders spin a silken line and launch themselves on a breeze, airborne on their way to a new home.

Nobody tells the spiderling when to leave the cocoon. Nobody tells it what to eat, when to molt, how to spin a thread of silk or what to do with that thread. Nobody teaches a young orb spider to weave a web or any spider how to shape an egg cocoon. They know these things, instinctively, as a hatchling fish knows how to swim. And they know how to kill an insect with their poison fangs, and how to hide from enemies. But they don't know how to think, and to the best of our knowledge they know neither happiness nor sorrow.

A spider, in other words, is a completely efficient small machine endowed with a spark of life. It is such a machine from the time it hatches from the egg, needing no instruction, complete with all necessary instincts and reflexes. It is—

I interrupt for a moment, because at this very instant a tiny brown spider has dropped from a bookcase above my desk and is hurrying across a typed page here at my elbow. He did not actually drop; he came down a silken line that he spun as he came, and that line is so fine that I can see it only in precisely the right light.

He has abandoned the line. He runs across the page, and I halt him with a pencil point and see that he is exactly as long as the letter *m* on my typewriter. That is slightly less than one eighth of an inch. Yet in this small body are packed not only the organs necessary for living but all the instincts and reflexes common to spiders. There is every reason to believe that this small spider here on my desk is substantially the same as are the fossil spiders found in rocks nearly 300 million years old.

The spider has crossed the typed page, reached the edge of the desk, found a satisfactory anchorage for its line, and now is dropping to the floor, paying out another silken line as it goes. It is something like a mountain climber going down a rope from a cliff, except that the spider makes its own rope as it goes. Its kind have been doing this ever since there were cliffs to be descended here on earth, and much, much longer than there have been desks and men to use them. Yet no spider has ever yet evolved enough brain to know that this is a desk and that the object on the floor where he will land is a human foot that can move two inches and put an end to that spider's life.

That spider, I assume, is in some way aware of being alive. It has hungers and it has the instincts which tell it to spin silk and to mate and multiply. It has no awareness of death. It has little awareness of others of its own kind, apparently, except as rivals for food. It may have eaten other spiderlings in the cocoon before it emerged—many kinds of spiders are cannibalistic, from the time of hatching.

I can explain the spider by saying that nature has an infinite variety of life forms and that each one is, in its own time and place, sufficient unto itself. But that does not answer a persistent question: Why, then, has there been the kind of change that eventually created my own kind, man? If spiders were a satisfactory form of life 250 million years ago, why weren't fish satisfactory? True, fish are still fish, but there were some fish that became amphibians, and amphibians became reptiles, and reptiles became birds and mammals. Change persisted. But not for spiders.

The scorpion, for instance, is only a step or two, broadly speaking, from the horseshoe crab. The harvester is little more than an awkward, long-legged spider. None of them traveled far on the road of change, and they have traveled virtually no distance at all in many million years. There they are, a family of creatures that achieved a form and a way of life that was, for them, sufficient. They achieved it early, and the forces of change passed them by.

The Arachnida, the spider family, participate in this common inheritance, life, as I said somewhat earlier. But they are not even remotely of my own kind. Except that they move about and eat only organic matter, which makes them a part of the animal kingdom, they are almost as remote from me as the weeds that grow in my pastureland. Yet they are closer kin than the thistle and the pigweed, for they *are* animals, and so are men.

To me, they are significant for what they lack rather than

for what they possess. They have senses of taste, touch, sight, and perhaps of smell and hearing. But they use these senses only for the most fundamental kind of existence. They have reflexes and instincts, and a notably efficient means of using them. When threatened, many of them will defend themselves; others will try to escape. When hungry, they will kill and eat. But they have no sense of compassion, not even an instinct to protect others of their own kind. I have mentioned that spiderlings sometimes eat each other in the cocoon. If I find two spiders near each other in the grass and threaten one of them with a stick, that spider will often back off and try to defend itself; but the other spider is completely oblivious unless it is threatened directly.

No spider has any sense of parenthood. They do not feed the young, beyond what food is left over from the egg after hatching. Some spiders carry their young on their backs, but there is no evidence that this is by choice; it is, rather, because some instinct tells the young spiders to cling to the female for a time. And if there are too many young to find room on the mother's back, they are left to their own devices. Even those on the mother's back are not fed by her. As soon as they are big enough to eat, they leave her and fend for themselves. The female spider's instinct tells her only to form a cocoon and lay eggs in it; that is the extent of her instinctive motherhood. Spiders live only for themselves, and they show no sense of time beyond the immediate present. There is neither past nor future for a spider, only the now.

And there is no urge toward change. Whatever adaptation the arachnids have made seems to have been in the slow process of what we call natural selection. Those best fitted to survive in certain environments have survived and multiplied. If large size was important, the larger ones grew larger until they had reached the maximum size tolerated by their environment. If minuteness was called for by some special condition, the small ones became smaller. All without subjective plan or knowing. And always, apparently, the ratio of brain to body, of capacity for thought, remained at the constant minimum needed to carry out the orders of inherent impulses and reflexes.

The spider clan has its place in the complex organization of this world's life, and it clings firmly to that place. Without the spiders there would be an immediate upset in the balance that is so persistent and, at times, so baffling to man. Some spiders catch fish, some live on birds and small mice, but for the most part they live on insects, which are closer kin to them than are any other living creatures. But both the spiders and the insects live in a world that is enduringly strange to man. They surround us, they outnumber us beyond calculation, they are in terms of life itself remotely related to us. But they remain alien, mysterious in origin and understandable only as themselves, not as links or even as theoretical changelings, in the big web of life that stretches so far back in time.

Insects

Armor, Instinct and the Community

ONLY FOUR KINDS of animals have ever learned to fly, the insects, the now extinct flying lizards, the bats, and the birds. The insects were the first to take wing, before any of the others even existed. Quite possibly the power of flight enabled the insects to persist through thousands of centuries, for it made them able to escape earthbound enemies. Fossil insects almost 200 million years old have been found, and among the most ancient insect fossils are wings with no traces of the bodies that bore them.

Insects seem to have changed little over the eons. Many fossil insects are almost identical with those we know today, particularly cockroaches, dragonflies, certain beetles, ants and bees. Some of those ancients, I am sure, would be completely at home in my own woods and fields. There is every probability that ants and bees, at least, have been the kind of creatures they are, social instinct and all, as far back as we can trace them. And it is this social instinct, typical of many insect species, that makes them of special interest to men. Special, that is, beyond the simple fact that they, too, are examples of life, living creatures. And it is this social instinct that marks the distinct line between insects and the spider family, for the moment ignoring the anatomical differences so important to entomologists.

The social instinct is by no means common to all insects. Authorities in the field say that only twenty-four separate families of insects have ever evolved what are called "insect societies," and of these the ones best known today are the bees, the wasps, the ants, the termites and the beetles. A society calls for teamwork, some enduring instinct and ability to act as a group toward a common project. A swarm of flies or mosquitoes definitely is not a society; it is merely an unorganized group in which every individual is working for itself. A hive of bees or a hill of ants is a community, with assigned tasks for every member of the colony and an organized system of labor and existence.

Nobody knows how many species of insects there are and the number of individuals in each species is incalculable. A few years ago I estimated the number of ants marching in a forage column from a nest in the edge of a pasture. It was so inconspicuous a nest that I had never noticed it until the column marched out, one morning, to attack another ant colony about two hundred feet away. The attackers marched steadily for almost six hours in a column roughly five abreast, and I estimated the numbers at almost 25,000. I have no idea how many anthills there are on this farm, but if there were 25,000 ants in that one inconspicuous colony there must be many, many million ants within a hundred yards of the house.

Yet ants may not be the most numerous of the insect species.

Probably the various beetles vastly outnumber them, for there are about 22,000 species of beetles in North America alone and beetles live all over the world. And who could even begin to estimate the number of houseflies, say, or mosquitoes in even one small area? I doubt that we have comprehensible numbers to count them.

In the sense of sheer survival and proliferation, the insects are probably the most successful of all animals. There are various reasons. They have perfected a means of extracting oxygen from the air that is more efficient, for their purpose at least, than the lung-breathing of larger animals. Insects have a network of air tubes through their bodies which swiftly purifies their blood and provides them with quick, constant energy. Their power of flight and quick movement enables them to escape from many enemies. Many insects live on plants, and there is a great variety of plants; hence, the insects have profited by a diversity of opportunities for food and shelter. Insects, by having their skeleton on the outside of their bodies, are able to compress all the necessary organs for life into a very small space, so they can take advantage of the gaps, so to speak, between the living space and the vital needs of birds and quadrupeds. And, finally, insects have remarkably well-developed instinct.

It is this instinct that enables insects to react so quickly. They don't have to think what to do, as long as the situation is not too unexpected. Being unable to reason, they simply react as instinct tells them to. And instinct is built into them, as definitely as are their eyes or their antennae. They don't have to learn what to do. They simply know—or their nerves and muscles know.

And here we get over into the fascinating area of the social instinct of certain insects. I have never seen this discussed, but I am sure it is not a new or unique idea: Can it be possible that man's social instincts and actions came, not from the insects, but from the same common source? We don't know the source, but possibly it was the urge for common survival, for preservation of the species. That, at least, seems to be the purpose of the social instinct in social insects.

Such a notion, of course, raises many other questions. If ants and bees had this instinct millions of years ago, why did it not appear with any noticeable strength or persistence in the early amphibians, for instance? Or the reptiles? Why didn't the big lizards have it? And why do not other insects than those relatively few species who build colonies today have it?

And, further, if this instinct was strong enough to shape the lives and habits of social insects for many million years, why did it fail to evolve in them some advance in intelligence, some noticeable increase in reasoning power? The brain of an ant or a wasp or a bee seems to be ready-made, complete with instincts, as soon as the ant or wasp or bee emerges from the larval stage. It doesn't have to be taught anything. It cannot, in fact, be taught anything, not in the sense that we know teaching. It is born knowing all it needs to know, and it learns little from experience.

Insects are remarkably efficient, more so than most of the higher animals. The mouth of an ant or a bee, for example, is perfectly equipped to do everything an ant or a bee has to do. Possibly the insect learns to use that mouth more skillfully by practice, but from the very start it can do satisfactorily all it really needs to do. My own hands can do many more tasks than an ant's mouth can (in a sense, they are equivalent, since the ant's mouth parts are its nearest approximation of fingers), but my fingers are not adept from birth, and an ant's mouth is. I have to learn to use my hands. I, a man, am initially limited in my capacity and my skills, but eventually I become not only more adept but more broadly skillful. I, too, have instincts and reflexes, but to these have been added reasoning power and the ability to learn, to acquire new skills.

In many ways, insects are the most skillful of all nonhuman animals. Wasps knew how to make paper long before man learned, and the paper nests of the hornets are insulated against both heat and cold as well as being waterproof. Mud-dauber wasps are expert at building mud structures, though they have little sense of design beyond the patterns of crude utility. Ants made the first apartment houses, the first underground communities. Dung beetles make almost perfect spheres, balls in which they lay their eggs and which provide food for their young. Some wasps even know how to use tools; they use a large grain of sand to tamp down the earth over a cavity in which they have laid eggs. Some ants are farmers, masticating leaves into humus, planting fungus spores and harvesting food from the resulting growth. Bees make beautifully proportioned hexagonal cells in which to store honey and hatch eggs, though the precision of their hexagons is something less than perfection.

These skills I recognize and admire, but I know that they are a result of instinct, not reason. They are not acquired skills, and they are never really improved or perfected much beyond what they were in the insect when it was hatched. And this is a fact to remember when one considers the even more fascinating habits of social insects.

The social habits of bees and ants particularly have held man's interest and inspired his admiration for a long time. These insects seem so efficient! They know precisely what to do and how to do it. Their whole life seems completely dedicated to the community. Man has from time to time so admired this efficiency and dedication that he has wished he could achieve equal strength and unity in his own society.

But history indicates that this is not what man really wants. When he sees what it means, his intelligence rejects it. The purpose of the ant and the bee and the way of life of such insects, admirable as they may be in some ways, are not enough for man.

There are variations among the social insects, but the way of life of the ants illustrates the essentials of such organization and instinctive accomplishment. As a boy I spent many hours watching the big red ants of the West, those which build and occupy large conical mounds and harvest grass seed—and, I may add, have short tempers and vicious bites. Later I learned from more seasoned and systematic observers many details which I had not discovered for myself.

There is a rigid caste system in almost every ant colony. Most of the members are infertile females. They do the work of the colony, from gathering food and building the complex of nests and tunnels to caring for the eggs, the pupae and the larvae. The males are drones, and they are generally tolerated only because eventually one of them will fertilize a new queen. Sometimes the males are also the colony's soldiers, the fighters. The queen is the heart of the colony, pampered, petted, fed, and kept prisoner inside the nest. She lays all the eggs.

Periodically, new queens are hatched. At a proper time, the queens and the males grow wings, are released from the colony and take flight. The queens are mated in the air, return to the earth, nip off their wings, and find sites for new nests. The males die soon after the nuptial flight. Each solitary queen digs her way into the ground and begins to lay eggs. She tends them until the first ants are born, a generation of sexless females. They go to work, enlarge the nest, care for the queen (who never again emerges into the open), tend the eggs, feed the larvae, and live out their brief lives.

The scientists seem to agree that most ants have some capacity for pleasure and anger, that they apparently are elated at times and depressed at other times. They have keen senses, with good eyes which apparently cannot detect color but can see ultraviolet rays, which are invisible to man. They have "touch hairs" on the body that are sensitive to vibrations, which probably include sounds. It seems likely that they can communicate with each other by means of their antennae, though that communication probably is limited to news of food or danger. They are sensitive to heat and cold. There is no evidence that they feel pain; an ant with its whole abdominal section cut off will continue to eat honey with apparent relish.

There is evidence of a keen sense of community loyalty. Ants make raids on other communities for "slaves," and they fight battles in defense of their own nests. I have watched a number of such battles, which are individual combats on a mass scale. Ants are ruthless. They dismember each other, apparently with little effect until the maimed ant is left helpless. I have seen two ants, each with legs missing, push and tumble and nip at each other as though still whole. But if one succeeds in cutting off the other's antennae, the victim seems helpless. It stands dazed, it runs in circles, it staggers about nipping at the air. But it is out of the battle, finished, utterly defeated.

One researcher has said that 95 per cent of an ant's actions are purely instinctive, that 4 per cent are a result of habit formed in the community, and that only one per cent can be credited to anything like reflection or subintelligence. This one per cent, he adds, is "trifling" and can be perceived only by long observation. Another researcher says that he trained an ant to come and eat from his finger. Still another man reported that he had taught an ant to cross a bridge to reach its nest. But such instances are of virtually no consequence and verify, if anything, the statement that ants have trifling intelligence, though they are instinctively very skillful.

In every instance that I have ever seen—and I find no exceptions to this in researchers' reports—when an ant nest is disturbed the workers rush to save the pupae, the undeveloped young of the colony. They do not hurry away to save themselves. Self-preservation is not high among their instincts, but safety for the next generation is. And that probably is one reason the ants, as a species, have persisted for millions of years. The colony comes first, always. And that is true of all social insects. It is almost as though there were no individuals, but only cells or separate small parts of the colony, and the colony itself were the true individual.

There is the disconcerting part of any casual discussion of insects, particularly the social insects. Parallels keep intruding, and it makes no difference if many of those parallels are more apparent than real. Mankind's society has a superficial resemblance to that of the ants. It is a community, a group of individuals living together and having a more or less common purpose, the welfare of all its members. Why, then, would it not be a good thing to emulate the ants?

The flaw in such thinking is thought itself, the capacity for thought in man and the incapacity for it in the ant. Man is an individual as well as a member of the community. The ant has no individuality; it is merely a part of the community, a kind of cog in the great machine. The machine may have its own complexity, but it is essentially a complexity of numbers, not of ideas. And it is based on instinct, not on thought. The ant has no inkling of ever being anything but an ant, a bundle of instincts and reflexes. The unsexed female worker can never become a queen and a mother. She is fixed in status, unchangeable. She is a minute animal, of a kind that has not changed in millions of years, and she has a routine of tasks that are equally fixed, unchanging and unchangeable.

Man, on the other hand, is another kind of being entirely. He is capable of thought. He is more than mere animal, knows it, refuses to accept such status. He has a capacity for learning, for change, in other words. He has instincts which prompt his desire for survival, both as an individual and as a species, but he also has intelligence which tells him that mere survival is not enough.

The insects are altogether remarkable, both in their mysterious beginnings and in their efficiency as persisting examples of life. By all the logic of survival, they should have inherited the earth long ago. They are prolific beyond belief. A single aphid, for example, is capable of producing several tons of descendants in a few weeks, if all were to survive. Many insects care for their young almost as well as do any of the larger animals. They can live in almost any environment that any form of life can endure. Not as a group but as individual species, they have adapted to the whole range of natural conditions and to every change that has occurred for millions of years. Their food supply covers the entire span of organic material. They prey widely upon one another, they eat almost every type of vegetation, and they are parasites on each other and on other animals. Some of them hibernate. Some can go for months without food.

Yet the life span of the individual insect is relatively brief. Few of them live as long as a year and most of them no longer than a single season. On the other hand, the periodic locust spends fifteen years or more in the larval stage and underground; it emerges as an adult insect for only a few days or weeks, to eat and mate and create a din and lay eggs. Worker bees live only about six weeks during the Summer. The adult form of the May fly lives only a few hours or days, never eating, mates, lays eggs and dies.

Insects are prodigal with energy. The bumblebee would seem to be too big and awkward to fly on its comparatively small wings, but by beating them at the rate of 240 strokes to the second it accomplishes the seemingly impossible. The birds use vast amounts of energy in flight, but a sparrow makes only thirteen wing strokes per second, a wild duck only nine. Even the dragonfly beats its wings twenty-eight strokes per second, when it is not gliding on an air current. Such activity demands much energy, but most insects spend their whole lives finding food and eating and digesting it, and they have tremendously efficient digestive systems. And, as said before, their breathing arrangement is probably the most efficient of that in any living animal. They get all the oxygen they need to generate energy with a minimum of effort.

And, finally, insects apparently achieved this form of body efficiency long ago. They evolved into a form that was perfect to their own needs, and they have not diverged from that form noticeably over the centuries, or even over the eons. Some fossil cockroaches have longer antennae than those of today, but how much race energy was needed to shorten a pair of needlessly long antennae? Change apparently was not for the insects after they achieved a form that answered their needs. The whole life force was directed toward survival, and in that sense the insects have been more successful than any other kind of life we know except the unicellular creatures, which also reached early perfection of their own kind. Certainly the insects are the only greatly diversified form of life that has persisted so long without material change.

Is this a virtue, or is it high achievement? I have my doubts. It seems to me that change is a basic law of nature, change, diversity, possibly improvement. Of course, I could be speaking thus as a kind of animal that is himself a result of continuing and persistent change, and therefore I may be unduly biased. But I see few instances that point in any other direction.

On the other hand, by their very resistance to change the insects might be considered the most successful of all the living creatures we see around us. That would depend on what we mean by success. I cannot concede that mere survival is in itself success, or that resistance to biological change is necessarily evidence of victory over anything except change itself. We are dealing here with life, and life is—or should be—more than persistent existence. To me, it is. Otherwise, why should there be life at all? Such a concession would reduce all life to a meaningless level.

I can conceive of an insect colony as a kind of unit of life, a composite of many motile cells which are the individuals. I, too, am a kind of composite unit composed of many individual cells, some of which have limited mobility but always within the confines of my own body. But even if I grant such identity for the whole colony, say, of an ant community or a hive of bees, there still remains the question of the community purpose. Complex and efficient as it is, its total achievement is nothing more than a mass of instincts and reflexes all directed toward survival, toward perpetuation. A whole community of ants does not achieve enough thought to create anything more imaginative than the kind of ant colony that has been typical of their kind for eons. Even as a community, a kind of composite unit of life, no society of insects has ever evolved anything comparable to even the simplest of primitive man's arts. And there is no evidence of thought, either concrete or abstract, in even the best organized of the social insects, beyond that dubious one per cent of thought which one researcher grants to an ant. And even there the researcher himself terms that a trifling fraction, most difficult to discover.

Yet the insects did achieve many skills, and the social insects long, long ago did achieve an organized form of life that has a superficial resemblance to the kind of life man eventually adopted. That cannot be dismissed out of hand. Somewhere that instinct toward shared work and a common purpose must have originated. We can rationalize it in the ant and the bee as a remarkable means of race survival, but we cannot ignore it. We have the same impulse. We have enlarged and expanded it, and we have refined it with thought and conscious purpose, but something of it is there in the human background. To that extent we must recognize our link with those very old, almost totally different, and mysteriously originated creatures, the insects.

Butterflies and Moths

Caterpillar, Pupa and Wing

LAST EVENING when we went out at dusk to look at the flower garden two sphinx moths came and hovered like hummingbirds at the petunias. When we came into the house and turned on the light there was a flutter at a screened window where a luna moth was frantically beating its fragile light-green wings, trying to reach the light inside. This morning I see half a dozen monarch butterflies at the milkweed on the riverbank, and in the vegetable garden are four or five other butterflies searching for special plants on which to lay their eggs.

This is the season of the Lepidoptera, the scale-winged ones —moths and butterflies, which, fragile as they are, are to me among the most baffling of all insects. And in a sense they are the most reassuring, for though they answer few of the big questions science asks of life they do raise other questions that

153

should bedevil anyone who is tempted to make glib statements.

The differences between butterflies and moths, the two major divisions of Lepidoptera, are rather tenuous except to the specialists. Generally speaking, butterflies are creatures of the daylight and moths are creatures of the night. Butterflies have simple antennae and moths have complex ones, often feathery. Butterflies are usually more vividly colored than moths. Most butterflies fold their wings over their backs when at rest, and most moths rest with their wings outspread or folded close to their bodies. Otherwise the differences are not particularly obvious.

Both butterflies and moths go through equivalent stages of physical change, or metamorphosis. They lay eggs, the eggs hatch into caterpillars, the caterpillars become pupae or encased changelings, and the pupae become moths or butterflies. Among the butterflies, some adults never take food or drink and have only brief lives devoted entirely to mating, laying eggs, perpetuating the species. Other butterflies, as well as most moths, eat during the adult stage, and many of them have relatively long lives, some living throughout the year or even longer. In all instances the caterpillars are voracious eaters, often being what man considers a pest. And all of them go through those successive stages in the same sequence—egg, caterpillar, pupa, and winged adult.

The differences in these stages are so striking that the caterpillar seems, offhand, to be of quite a different species from the butterfly or moth. Outwardly they appear to have no relationship one to the other. There are other insects that go through equivalent stages of change, but nowhere else is the difference from one stage to the next so remarkable. How the Lepidoptera came to this complex and roundabout method of reproduction is a mystery of long standing.

In terms of geologic history the moths and the butterflies are old—not as old as some other insects, and probably much younger than the spiders, but old enough to be recognizable in some of the earlier fossil deposits. Fragile though they are, bits of Lepidoptera wings and other body parts have been found in the Tertiary rocks here in America, rocks perhaps sixty million years old. Such fossils prove that the butterfly, or the moth, was a winged creature at that time, not merely a crawling caterpillar in which was some remote possibility of flight. But the specialists hesitate to assign even a closely approximate date to the time when the butterfly presumably emerged from the broad, primitive insect family.

The wing is the ultimately distinctive feature of the moth or butterfly. The wings of other flying insects are thin, clear membranes strengthened by ribs and veins, and they have no covering. Basically the butterfly wing has the same structure, a thin chitin membrane supported by stiff, tubular "veins." But in the butterfly the wings are covered with minute scales arranged in an overlapping pattern, much like the shingles on a house or the scales on a fish. The scales help strengthen the wing. They also carry the coloring so characteristic of moths and butterflies, usually in the form of pigment but also, in iridescent butterflies, in the form of light-refracting prismatic ridges. As a boy I was told that if one rubbed even a few of the scales from a butterfly's wing it could not fly. This is not true, but if the scales are rubbed off, the wing is weakened and may easily be broken.

There are four wings on a butterfly or a moth, as there are on all winged insects. The Lepidoptera, however, use the pair on each side as one wing, not separately as the dragonfly does. This is done by overlapping or by an even more ingenious device of hooked bristles.

As a general rule, butterfly wing colors range from reds and oranges through white and yellow to green, blue and purple. Most moths are darker-colored, with much gray and brown, in keeping with their nocturnal habits. Having such large wings, butterflies fly with relatively slow wing strokes, very slow compared, for instance, with a honey bee's two to three hundred strokes per second. And none of them can fly very fast. The swallowtail butterfly can travel about twelve feet a second, at top speed. The white cabbage butterfly can manage only about half that speed. On the other hand, some of them can fly great distances. Monarchs often migrate from my area to the Southern states for the Winter, and large flights of monarchs have been seen several hundred miles at sea.

Male butterflies are often more brilliantly colored than the females of the same species, though in some species this is reversed. When the female is larger or more brilliantly colored she usually courts the male and even carries him when they mate in the air. In many species the male has scent patches on the wings. This scent apparently is of great importance in mating, for it attracts the females, often from long distances. All butterflies appear to have a highly developed sense of smell.

A single mating, which always occurs in the air, is sufficient for the female to lay all her eggs. In most instances the male dies soon after mating and the female dies soon after she has laid her eggs. However, there are a few species that lay two sets of eggs each season and a very few that survive the Winter, usually in a kind of hibernation, and lay eggs in a second season. And among the moths there are a few species that are capable of parthenogenesis, the production of fertile eggs from an unmated, virgin female. (This is also true of some bees and ants and other insects.)

Thus far I have been discussing the adult butterfly or moth, the most conspicuous stage in the lepidopteran life cycle. But between the egg and the butterfly or moth occur other stages, all of which are quite remarkable.

The eggs are laid, without exception, on or near a source of food for the caterpillars that will hatch from them. The choice of such a food source is unerring. Monarch butterflies lay their eggs on milkweed plants. Cabbage butterflies lay their eggs on some member of the cabbage family. Clothes moths lay their eggs on wool or some other animal fiber, to man's constant annoyance.

The eggs hatch, usually in a matter of days, and the infant caterpillars begin to feed. Caterpillars are incessant feeders with tremendous appetites. The caterpillar of the Polyphemus moth, an American moth of the silkworm family, weighs only one twentieth of a grain when it is hatched. By the time it is fifty days old this caterpillar will have eaten fifty oak leaves, about three quarters of a pound. This amounts to 86,000 times as much as the caterpillar's original weight. If a human child weighing eight pounds at birth were to eat as much, proportionately, it would consume 344 *tons* of food. Even if one takes fifty years of human life as the equivalent of fifty days in a caterpillar's life, this would mean that the child, and the adult it becomes, would eat nearly seven tons of food a year for fifty years, almost forty pounds a day, thirteen pounds at a meal three times a day.

The caterpillar has no resemblance to the moth or butterfly it will become. It has six true legs, as do all insects, but it has additional claws that serve as legs when it crawls about. It has six simple eyes. Usually, but not always, it has hairs that probably serve some sensory function, as they do in the adult moth or butterfly. It has a mouth equipped for biting, chewing or tearing food. In most moth caterpillars there is also a gland in the mouth that secretes material for spinning a silken thread, an arrangement much like the spinnerets on a spider but situated at the opposite end of this creature. Its body is quite different, both internally and externally, from that of the butterfly or moth which laid the egg from which the caterpillar hatched. It has no sexual organs. It has no wings, even in a rudimentary stage, though it does have "imaginal disks," as the entomologists call them, which eventually evolve into wings. It is essentially an elongated intestinal tract, an eating machine. Its function is to eat and grow.

The caterpillar sheds its skin as it grows. After a series of molts it becomes as big as it will ever be, and at a proper time it "hibernates." It either spins a silken cocoon around itself or becomes encased in a tough shell called a chrysalis. Most moths form cocoons, and most butterflies form chrysalises. The cocoon or chrysalis is usually attached to a hospitable place for the adult, winged form to be when it emerges.

Inside this pupal case, whether it is a cocoon or a chrysalis, the original caterpillar changes form completely. New organs evolve. Old parts waste away, almost as though diseased. Wings appear, folded close against the new body. The complete form of the winged creature takes shape. Finally, when its time has come, the pupal case splits open and this new insect appears.

The moth or butterfly crawls into the open air, and its antennae, complete and ready to function, stretch out. It stretches its legs, crawls onto some support. The wings, soft and moist and useless at the time of emergence, begin to unfold. The new creature, fat with body fluids, pumps a large part of those fluids into the wing veins, stretches the wings and slowly fans them in the air. The wing membranes dry and stiffen. The body shrinks, relieved of its distending excess of fluid. The large, complex eyes (the eye of a nocturnal moth may have as many as 27,000 facets, incredibly more complex than any caterpillar's eye) look around. The antennae wave, feel the air, come into full use of their mysterious senses. And when the wings are fully dry and set, this moth or butterfly flies out into the world, a new creature, something almost totally different from the sluggish caterpillar that was its immediate progenitor.

This elaborate process, this whole series of processes, is well known to the entomologists. It has repeatedly been observed and is fully tabulated. Any layman with a little knowledge can go into the woods or fields in early Spring, find a cocoon or a chrysalis, bring it home, and watch the whole emergence. There is no deep mystery about it—no mystery at all except why it happens, what pattern, what system or order, what rhythm of change, has dictated and dominated it. Compared to this happening, the emergence of a chick from an egg, in itself a marvelous thing, is simplicity itself, for the chick is a miniature of the creature that laid the egg. Here we have a totally different event. A butterfly laid an egg. That egg hatched into a caterpillar with no hint of flight or winged beauty. That caterpillar retired into a cocoon or a chrysalis, and out of that house of change now comes a fragile-winged creature of the air, a living bit of sheer beauty and imagination.

Why should this happen? Why should it happen in precisely this way? I find no explanation in the facts of evolution, none that convinces or even persuades. In some instances, such as that of the frog, evolutionary history seems to be recapitulated in the changes from egg to adult. The tadpole stages seem to duplicate the fundamental changes from a minute, water-dwelling creature through tailed and gill-breathing forms up to the stage of emergence onto the land. Those changes are obvious and understandable. There is a parallel recapitulation of evolutionary stages in the growing fetus of the mammal. But, even if I were to grant that, eons ago, a crawling caterpillar did become a fragile, winged butterfly by some mysterious command of change and evolution, I should still be baffled by that pupal stage, that amazing transformation which occurs, without exception, inside the chrysalis. I can see no recapitulation of evolution at that point. It is sheer mystery, even though the specialists have investigated it and have their own explanations. The explanations tell what happens, and in a sense they tell how it happens. But I look in vain for any word of why it happens.

There is another factor in this matter of the moths and caterpillars that seems to have no explanation that really satisfies. This one is further back, in the egg itself. Ignore, at this point, the purpose of the egg and the process of its origin in the female, its fertilization by the male, its whole cycle, and look at the egg.

Moth and butterfly eggs are small, some so small they can be identified by the naked eye only as egg masses. Others are the size of a pinhead, some even larger. They have membranous shells or outer coverings, which protect them from the cold or the desiccation of drought. They come in many shapes. Some look like barrels, some like simple rods or bars, some are cones, some are hemispheres, some are like cheeses and some like turbans. The shape varies with the species but it never varies within the species.

On the surface of these minute eggs are patterns. Some of them can be seen vaguely with the naked eye, but most require the help of at least a ten-power magnifying glass, or even a microscope, to be seen clearly. On some of these lepidopteran eggs there are ridges, or grooves, or indentations. Some have patterns of raised lines, in a network of geometrical design. Some are like miniature carved jewels. And they are of many colors—blue, brown, red, green, yellow, white. Sometimes they are marked only by those ridged lines, but sometimes they are patterned with color, with microscopic dots. And in every instance the lines and the dots of color are in symmetrical patterns.

There is no evidence that these lines or ridges are lines of cleavage when the eggs hatch. On the contrary, the intricate patterns tend to fade and vanish as the eggs approach the time of hatching. There seems to be no physical purpose for these details of color or shape or decoration.

I can understand the coloration of birds' eggs, at least up to a point. The eggs of shore birds are particolored in a way that makes them look almost exactly like seashore pebbles, and there is protective coloration, or at least coloration that to some extent matches the background of the nesting place. But why are the eggs of the Lepidoptera not only colored but decorated, often "carved" like the most minute cameo work? Why are they patterned in the most intricate and even microscopic detail and perfection of design? Whence came those patterns, and do they have a purpose?

There are other patterns in nature, many of which have obvious purposes. Seeds are patterned and usually they are symmetrical, even to coloration. The spurs, hooks and buoyant hairs on seeds are clearly there to assist in distribution of the species, and the symmetry, even in the placement of the fluff or the spines, is in keeping with the general rule of symmetry and balance, as is the round or oval form of many seeds.

Birds, animals, reptiles, fish and insects are often patterned in what we call protective coloration. The zebra's stripes, the leopard's spots, the speckled wings of the night hawk, the stripes and spots of the snakes all appear to be in keeping with the usual habitat of such creatures, the natural patterns of light and shadow or the vegetation. We have plausible explanations which generally satisfy.

In the inanimate world nearly all minerals have crystalline forms in clearly defined pattern and color. These forms, we are told, are a consequence of the atomic structure, and any decorative or aesthetic quality they may have is incidental and primarily based on internal stresses. And aesthetics, of course, are of human invention, an intellectual or emotional response to form, shape and color. These things I know and can accept. But when I look at mineral crystals I do wonder why the internal stresses manifest themselves in just this way. Physical explanations are not quite sufficient. There must be some pattern governing those stresses.

And when I come to the patterns, the sheer decoration, of the eggs of butterflies and moths I find no reason that lies in the realm of logic. There they are, those minute flecks of potential life, decorated in beauty that seems to have no mechanical, utilitarian purpose. Functionally, those eggs would be, or should be, as effective in conveying the germ of life from one generation to the next if they were spherical, colorless, undecorated beads of fertile jelly. But the fact remains that they are not.

So we would seem to have come down to a point that reaches beyond the usual matter of function, and at that point the whole question arises whether function is the total answer to life. I doubt that it is.

We are so much in the habit of dissecting and interpreting everything in terms of function and physical cause that we sometimes lose sight not only of the wonder of life but of the possibility of factors beyond the cold factuality. I see a pasture rose in bloom at the edge of my meadow, its five broad, silken petals a delight to the eye. It is a thing of beauty, self-grown, self-patterned. Then I remember that I have been told that those petals evolved to serve as landing platforms for the insects that serve as pollinating agents and that their color attracts those insects. The whole purpose of that rose, I remember, is to invite pollination, produce fertile seeds, and grow another plant of its own kind. That is the factual explanation. It is perfectly true, as far as it goes. But, I wonder, does it go far enough? I even wonder about myself: Is it enough that the human brain should learn how a rose accomplishes the obvious purpose? Is the obvious purpose enough of an answer to my sense of wonder and question? Is it enough to know that the rose evolved from some other plant, some basic divergence of a plant form many thousands of years ago, and that its blossom is a complex form of male and female organs? Or is there something beyond that I vaguely sense, some pattern beyond that of the rose?

Perhaps the fact itself is enough; but I wonder. It may be that the fact is only one part of a far greater whole. Perhaps we see too little and believe too grudgingly when we seek processes and meanings. Processes are the "how," not the "why."

The Lepidoptera, the moths and butterflies, are only insects, members of a vast and persistent branch of small-scale life. They are, in their adult stage, symbols of frivolity and the transience of life. Yet they have been here a long, long time, and still we do not know why that amazing change occurs between the caterpillar and the gay-winged butterfly, that metamorphosis inside the chrysalis. And, even more mysterious to me, we do not know why such a simple thing as a butterfly's egg should be shaped and decorated as it is. We have no explanation, not even a factual one.

We do not know. That is one reason the very presence of butterflies and moths is important—to remind us, in odd hours, that there are things we do not know, reasons we cannot even guess, patterns that have no factual purpose we have yet discovered.

Life—
Flesh and Blood

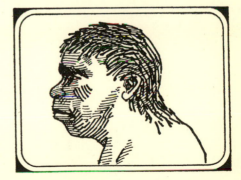

Fish

The First Backbone

I HAVE BEEN out on the river capturing cold-blooded, strictly aquatic, water-breathing, craniate vertebrates whose limbs are developed as fins and whose long, tapering bodies are covered with scales and end in broad, vertical caudal fins. In other words, I have been fishing. I came back with four yellow perch, and because I am a carnivorous animal I am going to eat fried fish. That is one advantage of living beside a river. Another advantage is that I have members of the oldest vertebrate family on earth as near neighbors.

According to the paleontologists, the earliest fish evolved about 390 million years ago. They lived in the Silurian period, when most of the earth's land was still under water and before the first land plants were here. I find it interesting, though not of immediate importance, that fossil evidence indicates there were spiders and scorpions at that time too, apparently the first forms of visible life that lived on land and breathed air.

Fish began and always have been aquatic. As I read the story, somewhere along the path of evolution one of the simplest forms of aquatic life developed a central core, a rodlike, gristly form of bodily support for the glob of protoplasm of which it consisted. Over the eons this gristly rod became a primitive backbone. Then this creature, which had absorbed the oxygen from its surrounding water through wrinkles in its surface, extended those wrinkles into slits. Those slits were the first gills. Through them the creature could take in water, absorb the oxygen it needed, and expel the water. With gills and the beginning of a backbone, this ancient creature was ready to become a fish, or at least a near-fish.

This process of evolutionary change had taken millions of years, but it eventually produced the Ostracoderm. Paleontologists have tentatively reconstructed the Ostracoderm from scanty fossil clues. It seems to have been a creature with a horseshoe-shaped head covered with horny plates and with a tail something like that of a modern skate. Only the horny plates have been found among the fossils. The Ostracoderm probably was a sluggish creature that lived on the bottom of warm, shallow, fresh-water seas. The supposition is that it absorbed its food, since it seems to have had no jaws.

The importance of this phase of evolution, in big terms, was the development of a gristly core, the beginning of a backbone, and the beginnings of a brain and a spinal cord. In a primitive sense, that was the origin of sharks, fish, amphibians, and the animals which eventually produced man.

When I go out on the river and catch fish I am not actually dipping back hundreds of millions of years into time, except in a figurative sense. Today's fresh-water fish are relatively modern. Among salt-water fish the sharks, with their gristly backbones, are probably the oldest type of fish we know today, in any number at least. The very ancient ones are known, if at all, only by their rare and extremely fragmented fossil remains. In terms of time, the dragonflies that seine gnats from the air over the river are much older in approximately their present form than any fish I shall ever catch.

The fish I catch, like all early forms of life, are what we call cold-blooded. Their body temperature is approximately the same as that of the water around them. This is an efficient arrangement because it enables the fish to get along with a minimum of oxygen. They use relatively little oxygen to warm the body. It is a system so efficient that it has persisted in most of the life on this earth, notably in insects, fish, amphibians and reptiles. And in plants, of course. Only mammals and birds evolved the more complex system of burning oxygen to maintain a body temperature different from that of their immediate environment.

I hesitate to say that the change to warm-bloodedness in birds and mammals was a step upward. All anyone can truthfully say is that it was a change, a variation from the old system, and that it must have had some purpose. The most obvious purpose was to enable warm-blooded creatures to increase their mobility and their range. It also had one obvious disadvantage. It made necessary the consumption of more food and more oxygen. And it demanded some means of insulating the warm-blooded body against variations in external temperatures. Aquatic mammals developed a layer of insulating fat. Most land animals developed a coat of fur. And birds developed feathers.

Fish escaped that problem. Their dominating necessity, both as individuals and as a species, was to escape other live enemies and to perpetuate the species. From the primitive bony plates, which served as a kind of external skeleton in the Ostracodermi, the fish evolved a kind of body armor, scales. This armor somewhat protected them from their enemies. In some species the scales took fantastic shapes—horns and spines and other forbidding types of armor or armament—that made them more difficult to attack.

The nearest thing to these defenses that I find on my river fish is the catfish's horns. The catfish wears a pair of sharp horns flanking its mouth and a particularly vicious horn on its dorsal fin. The sunfish, of course, and all members of the bass family also have spines on their fins, but these are essentially minor defensive equipment. Compared to some of the bristly, spiny, weirdly armed ocean fish, these river fish are as commonplace and defenseless as guppies. But they remind me, every time I catch one, every time I gut or fillet a perch or a trout and see its skeleton and its remarkable adaptation to its environment, that though evolution is a long-enduring and continuous process, it usually arrives at a practical result. No man has ever evolved a more efficient shape for underwater travel than the basic shape of a fish.

The fresh-water portion of my river, which I know best, probably is home to no more than twenty-five or thirty different kinds of fish. This is only a minute sampling of the more than 25,000 known and identified species of fish in the world. Excepting only insects, fish have evolved more variations in kind than any other kind of visible animal life. And in total numbers, fish easily outnumber all other species except possibly insects.

In fish I can see the origins of my own backbone and skeleton, and in their gills I can see the evolutionary start of my own lungs. Equally remarkable, to me, is the system of reproduction which, in one way or another, is typical of virtually all the animal life I know and can see. The basic factor of that system is the egg, and the basic elements are the two separate sexes.

The earliest forms of life propagated by division of themselves. This ultrasimple process never was abandoned. It persists today in such elementary forms of life as the protozoa, the sponge, and some parasitic worms. We speak of them as "low" in the evolutionary scale, though "low" may not be the correct word. They are essentially simple, but that simplicity was so efficient for their purpose that they stabilized with that system long ago and never changed it.

Other forms of life, which we call "higher," evolved a variant on that system of division. Out of that variant eventually came the differentiated sexes. Instead of dividing the original body, as protozoa do, into approximately equal parts, each of which contained half the original nucleus, the new form of life evolved a means of separating minute parts from the parent body, each part containing a germ of new life. These minute parts eventually became what we call eggs. But the egg process was still more complex, because two parts, quite different from each other, were needed to generate life—the fractions we know as male and female, sperm as well as egg.

These separate parts developed early in some kinds of life. In certain protozoa we still find what zoologists call microgametes and macrogametes, the equivalent of the two sexes. At a certain stage, protozoa produce both these forms. Neither by itself can develop into new protozoa, but if pairs of them come together, one microgamete and one macrogamete, they fuse and continue the life cycle as new protozoa, capable themselves of reproducing.

Somehow this process of differentiation and pairing was carried over into other forms of evolving life, and male and female appeared. The female was able to produce eggs, minute portions of her own vital center, and the male could produce sperm, even smaller parts of his own vital element. When egg and sperm came together, a fertilized egg was the result. And the fertilized egg eventually grew into a new individual.

The earliest forms of fish apparently had this system of differentiated sexes and reproduction by an egg-sperm process. The fish I catch today still have it, in substantially the same form that fish have had it for many millions of years. The female produces eggs, vast quantities of them. Codfish lay two to four million eggs a year and large cod have been taken with roes estimated to contain as many as nine million eggs. When I catch a female sunfish in late Spring or Summer she usually contains a fat pair of roe which sometimes weigh a sixth as much as her whole body. And the male sunfish have pouches of sperm, the milt, a third to a half as big as the roes in the females.

Most fish lay vast numbers of eggs because the rate of survival is so low. It is estimated that fewer than five cod eggs out of a million hatch and mature. I suspect that the hatch-and-survival rate of my river fish, even the sunfish, is somewhat higher, but I would put the figure at less than one in 10,000. If it were much higher than that, my river would be bank-full of fish in a very few years.

The ordinary fertilization of fish eggs is far from efficient. The female lays the eggs and the male spreads the sperm in a milky cloud which, if conditions are right, sweeps over the eggs, fertilizing all those it reaches. But a chance current or any one of a dozen other hazards can dissipate the sperm before it reaches the eggs. Even fertilized eggs do not all hatch. Most fish eat eggs, even of their own kind. And those which hatch still face fearful hazards because most fish also eat smaller fish, and so do birds, turtles, water snakes and many other predators. The profligate laying of eggs is the only means of insuring survival of the species.

But less hazardous means of reproduction apparently have been evolving even in fish. At least one can say that other means than the broadcasting of eggs and sperm in the same area have been and still are being tried. In some fish—skates, for instance—the female has been impregnated with the male sperm before she lays the eggs. In still others—rays, for instance, at one end of the size scale, and guppies at the other— the fertilized eggs are held inside the mother until they hatch.

Sea perch have what amounts to a gestation period, almost like that in mammals, and bear live young several months old and sometimes one-sixth as long as the mother.

But the fresh-water fish here in my river are quite common-place and conventional in these matters. The females lay the eggs, the males spread the milt around them, and enough of them hatch to keep the warm shallows teeming with clouds of young through the hot days of late Summer. And the fish popu-lation of the river appears to be fairly constant, though some years the rock bass and the sunfish are everywhere and other years the yellow perch gain ascendancy. There are always a few trout in the Spring, a modest population of black bass in the Summer, and an occasional pickerel all the year around.

Each year we go a few times to watch the sunfish on their spawning beds. There is one particular shallow backwater where the afternoon sun makes the water tepid and where, in the right light, we can anchor the boat and watch the fish for an hour.

The water in this particular cove is about two feet deep. Sun-fish gather there, just back from the main current of the river. The males fan out saucer-shaped nests, hollows twice the length of the fish who build them and perhaps an inch or an inch and a half deep. The male sunny, head up, tail down, sweeps out this nest with his tail, sweeps the bottom clean. The water clears. The male waits, challenging every other male who swims near. Then a female appears. The male welcomes her, swims around her, seems to urge her down onto the nest. She inspects it. If she approves, she comes to rest there and lays her eggs, which are like tiny golden-yellow beads. Eggs laid, she has done her job. She swims away. The male swims down over the nest and releases his sperm, a milky cloud of it which slowly settles over the eggs. Then he takes his stand over the nest and waits until the eggs hatch. If any other fish, male or fe-male, approaches the nest, the owner puts up a fight, rushing, slapping, crowding, trying to drive the other away from the eggs.

Sunfish eggs, like those of all the bass tribe, hatch in three or four days. Another two or three days and the young, which are about the size of a fragment of toothpick, are swimming about. Sometimes the parent, always the father, leads them to shallow water, where they will live—if they aren't gobbled up by some invader—for weeks, growing and preparing for deeper water and a broader life. But often the father deserts both nest and young as soon as they are swimming freely. Both the small-mouthed and largemouthed bass take care of their young for a week to a month, fighting off all foragers, herding the school of youngsters from shoal to shoal, being model parents.

The sunfish we watch in that shallow cove are usually in all stages of parenthood, some building nests, some waiting for a female, some guarding eggs, some ready to desert the hatch. Among them there is a vigorous belligerence. Most of them will fight all comers, and many of them are so touchy that they will snap at even a bare hook if it is tossed in among them. Before we found that this was a favorite nesting place, we occasionally tossed a line in there to see what would happen. Any warm afternoon we could catch a pailful of bluegills in half an hour, many of them six inches or more long and tasty pan fish. Then we found out why and stopped fishing there. It is more fun to watch them than to catch them. Besides, that nesting area provides food for the trout, the bass and the big yellow perch we catch. And those fish don't need our help to keep the sunfish down to a proper balance in the river's population.

My fresh-water fish are really throwbacks, in a sense, because the first fish are supposed to have evolved in fresh water. They came along in the procession of life before the oceans were salt, as they are now. The salt-water fish of today are varieties that adapted themselves to the gradually changing character of the ocean's water. Even the coelacanth, which has been called a "living fossil" because it is the only known link between fish and amphibians, once was a fresh-water fish, the chief predatory animal on earth during its heyday. The coelacanth, one of a family called fringe-fins, still persists as a salt-water fish, though it is so rare that until a few years ago it was believed to have vanished millions of years ago and was known only in fossil form.

A close relative of the coelacanth is the lungfish, which has an air bladder that serves as a lung and can live out of water for a considerable length of time. It also has nostrils that open into the mouth cavity, though it apparently does not breathe through them.

Both the coelacanth and the lungfish are considered remnants of the remote past, but they indicate lines of evolution. The coelacanth's fins are like rudimentary limbs, even to the bone structure. The lungfish's air bladder is a primitive lung. These two attributes were essential for the development of the first amphibian, and the first amphibian was a step toward all the land-dwelling animals, toward reptile, bird, mammal and man. But before either coelacanth or lungfish became an amphibian, it was a fish, a fresh-water fish.

When I watch the sunfish nesting, or when I hook and play and land a smallmouth or a brookie or bring a fat yellow perch to the net, I am seldom thinking of coelacanths or those remote ancestors of that ancient creature. But sometimes, on a warm Summer afternoon, I sit on the riverbank and watch that flow of water between its green banks and wonder if I am not seeing a kind of stream of evolving life in this river that flows past my dooryard. Life began in the fresh-water oceans, true, but by the time it had progressed to that stage of organization where backbones and brains and vestigial limbs were somewhere hidden in the structure of a fish, there was land and there were rivers. And those rivers and the shallow tidal waters at their mouth teemed with such life.

Fish evolved for life in the water, which then was the major element, excepting only the air which enveloped this earth.

Water, the great solvent, contained all manner of materials for life's creation and substenance. And, through the agency of lesser life, it provided the vital food for these strange, new creatures whose framework was made of calcium and whose flesh was essentially protoplasm enforced with carbon and hydrogen.

Why, I wonder, watching the river, did one of those fish choose to leave that hospitable water? What urgency was upon it to climb out onto the land, into the air? Was it to escape predatory enemies, or was it to achieve greater freedom? What was that urgency?

I don't know the answers. I doubt that anyone knows. All we know of a certainty is that other forms of life already had left the water-womb. Plants were growing in the humid air and marshy ground at the water's edge. Spiders and scorpions were there upon the land, eight-legged precursors of the insect armies that would eventually appear. But there were no other animals of enduring consequence except in the water. Yet from those fish, those early backboned creatures, came the hordes of land animals.

I sit on the riverbank and see the emergence, the long, slow change that evolved the first amphibians, the ages when that whole cosmos of marshland was dominated by those awkward newcomers of such a long history. The amphibians, then the first reptiles, then the age of reptile giants—dinosaurs, plesiosaurs, pterodactyls, ichthyosaurs and all the other unbelievable ones. I see them, in the steaming giant-fern jungles long before today's trees appeared; and somewhere among them, unheeded, I see the insignificant beginnings of the mammals, creatures no bigger than rats, but land animals and no longer reptiles. Animals whose blood ran warm and whose brains kept approximate pace with their bodies. There was the beginning of my own kind.

But first there were fish.

Amphibians

Venture onto Dry Land

MY REMOTE GREAT-UNCLES were croaking last night, down along the river. I have no qualms about recognizing the frogs as among my kinfolk; there is no way I can deny the relationship if I accept the basic theses about evolving life. First came the minute, single-celled water dwellers, so small and so remote that I have to take them on faith. Eventually, out of their eons of change, came the first fish. And when a creature that had once been a water-breathing fish crawled out onto the new land and made an effort to live there, the first amphibian appeared. That amphibian pioneered the way of all creatures of the land and the air except the microbes and the insects, which followed a separate line of evolution. My line led through the newts and the salamanders, and so did that of the frogs and the toads.

The frogs are still amphibious, and I am not. The line which led to me led to all the mammals and birds. The frog's line was a kind of amphibious dead end. In a sense, the frog is a holdover, a thoroughly successful one but an antique animal for all that and one of a vastly diminished breed. There are only three kinds of amphibians left in today's world, wormlike creatures called Caeciliae or blindworms, tailed creatures that we know as newts and salamanders, and tailless ones that make up the kingdom of frogs and toads.

I have no blindworms for neighbors, and I must say that I do not miss them. They are very primitive and of interest only to zoologists and students of the fine points of evolution. I do number frogs and toads, newts and salamanders among my local acquaintances. The frogs and the toads even qualify as friends, from my viewpoint at least. They are among the best four-legged neighbors I have. The newts and the salamanders stir only a rather distant academic interest in me. They are sluggish, unobtrusive and, except in a vague sense, uninteresting.

I suppose this attitude labels me as whimsical, especially in any discussion of evolutionary trends, since the frogs are off the main track. But I do have my reasons. Though the newts and the salamanders lie on the main stream of evolution toward my own kind, they never got beyond a minor station along that great river. They are essentially as they must have been many millions of years ago. To me, they represent an adventure that never got anywhere.

Now and then I find a newt in a damp, woody hollow or a boggy spot warm and wet with Spring. Nearly always it is a murky, overcast day when I find a newt, because a dry, sunny day makes life in the open difficult for him. His skin must remain moist or he is in trouble. His kind left the water to live on land a good part of the time, but dry land and dry air are still hazardous for his limited range of life.

The newts I know best are only a few inches long, are a dull coral color and crawl about among the wet, decaying leaves. I find them when swamp violets come to bloom and in those moist areas where such violets grow. Sometimes I turn over a flat stone on a hillside above the bogland and find a cowering newt beneath it. When I do, this dull creature looks around stupidly and wanders off on four weak legs, looking for another moist spot in which to hide.

I know this is no way to regard a creature which carries the remote beginnings of my own backbone and my own brain, not to speak of my own five fingers. But the span between us is too long for my impatient mind to bridge easily.

Once in a while, too, I find a salamander down along the river, and now and then I hook one while I am fishing in a shallow, murky cove. This fellow is a mud puppy, an amphibian who breathes through gills and directly through his skin. Though an amphibian, he spends little time on land. He never progressed even as far as the newt. All the salamanders I know are unexciting and uninteresting, primitive and dull.

The frogs and toads are in a wholly different category. They are here the year around, though they hibernate in Winter. From April till November I see and hear them every day. They are lively creatures, even the sluggish toad that haunts the garden. They have no visible resemblance to the lizardlike salamanders and I do not think of them as true primitives. They are cold-blooded, they breathe a part of their time directly through their skin, and they have no immediately visible link to my kind of animal. But I feel a kinship with them, or at least a degree of understanding. They belong in my world, as the fish belong, and the birds. Newts and salamanders are of another kingdom. Or so they seem.

All amphibians are generally considered as an experimental outgrowth of the ancient fish tribe. Considered as an experi-

179

ment, the amphibian was a success even though it was essentially a transition stage. It led to other animal forms, notably the mammals and birds of today.

But the use of the word "experimental" is both arbitrary and inexact, because evolution is a matter of change in various directions and most of the changes seem to have been dictated by some factor of environment. It is presumptuous to call any such change experimental, if only because we are not sure of the causes and we can judge evolution only by its results. There have been many changes. Some of them led down what seem to us to have been blind alleys because they often led to extinction. The word "experimental" implies conscious purpose, and I doubt that anyone can say either that there was or that there was not conscious purpose in any evolutionary change.

We now hear much talk about mutations caused by the effects of atomic radiation. Our immediate concern is with the fate of the human race, but our scientists are turning up data and theories that undoubtedly apply to the whole history of evolution. In surveying man-made radiation and comparing it with natural radiation they come up with sometimes controversial data, but the net result is more knowledge of what obviously has been happening in the universe for more time than man can measure. If man-made radiation can effect mutations or even affect genetics noticeably over the generations, it is obvious that natural radiation must have been doing the same thing, though probably at a somewhat slower pace, ever since the world began. Cosmic rays are still bombarding the earth and every form of life upon it.

Nuclear change has been going on since time began, and such change has always affected the forms of life, altered life in many ways. Evolution has not been a simple process of logical change, though natural selection has inevitably accompanied all change. With variations occurring constantly, many of them perhaps a result of nuclear bombardment, those variants best suited to current conditions of food and climate have survived and multiplied and those least suited have perished.

Perhaps the amphibians were "experimental," then, in a cosmic sense. Perhaps they were variants, created by some obscure radiation; and because they were suited to survival on land, which was then fortunately becoming habitable, they persisted. This is no more than the broadest kind of speculation, but it underlines the fact that we still have not learned all there is to know about evolution.

In any case, the first amphibians did appear and left the water to spend a part of their lives in the open air on the land. These creatures had inherited from their aquatic ancestors a primitive means of breathing air, they had backbones for bodily stability, and they had legs to support their bodies without the buoyancy of surrounding water.

We know very little about those early amphibians, but we do find a kind of condensed version of their life and the slow process of change in the way a modern amphibian's eggs hatch and evolve into a living, adult animal. The history of a frog, for instance, shows all the changes we could logically expect in the development of a fish into an animal capable of living most of its life on land.

The egg of a frog is in many ways like a fish egg, comparable in size and structure. It is laid in the water by the female frog, and it is fertilized there by the male, much as most fish eggs are fertilized. The egg hatches in about two weeks, the time depending somewhat on the temperature.

The egg hatches into a kind of larva which has neither mouth nor legs but does have three pairs of feathery external gills. Soon an opening appears for the mouth, and the larval tadpole is able to eat algae and other fine vegetable matter. Then four pairs of gill clefts open and the intestine begins to lengthen. Now the frog-to-be is able to swim by using its tail.

At this stage it becomes a true tadpole. A fold of skin grows over the external gills and new gills appear inside the gill slits. The mouth acquires horny jaws. Then the gill chambers close to a single small aperture through which water taken in at the mouth is expelled after the gills have absorbed its oxygen.

The tadpole grows steadily. Small "buds" appear on its body where the legs will grow. Both pairs of legs start at the same time but the hind legs develop first. As the hind legs grow the lungs appear, first as small pouches opening off the gullet. When the hind legs are fully developed the lungs are ready to work. The tadpole rises to the surface of the water and begins to breathe in gulps of open air. Then the forelegs begin to grow.

This has taken about two months, and every step of change has been in a precise order. As soon as the lungs begin to function other internal changes take place. The major changes now are in the heart and the circulatory system. As long as the tadpole breathed only through its gills it had a two-chambered heart, like a fish's heart. Two chambers are all that are necessary to that kind of life. But when the lungs began to work the heart developed a third chamber and the blood began to circulate through the lungs. This change in the tadpole is typical of the vital alteration from fish to terrestrial animal.

Now the tadpole is approaching its final form, the frog. The next step is to rid itself of the tail, by this time an awkward appendage and the last vestige of its fish ancestry. The blood begins to remove from the tail the materials the rest of the body can use. It is almost as though the tail had become diseased. It is absorbed from the inside and worn away from the outside, and finally it is sloughed off. Only a stub is left, and that eventually disappears.

The tadpole, born of an egg in the water, was first a kind of larva, then a kind of fish, and now it is a land animal that will drown if held under the water too long. Now it is a frog that will live on land most of its life, returning to the water only for safety from predators on the land and to lay eggs and perpetuate its kind in the parent element, water. It breathes with lungs, no longer has gills. But it also breathes through its skin, as did its ancestors before the first fish evolved gills. When the frog works its way into the autumn mud to hibernate it will breathe entirely through its skin throughout the Winter, thus reverting to the remote, primitive processes.

So there is my amphibian neighbor, the frog. That is, as near as we know, the way it first became a frog, not only the frog I know but the first frog that ever was. There, too, is the toad in my garden, which differs from the frog of the riverbank primarily in being a much uglier creature, in having a warty skin instead of a smooth one, and in spending all its life on dry land except for the brief period of egg-laying and mating. There were toads even on the virtually waterless high plains of eastern Colorado where I grew up. They dug holes in the ground in which to escape the blistering heat of Summer days, and they emerged at night to feed. They hibernated in the ground all Winter. Spring always created a few shallow pools of snow melt and rain water, and the toads gathered at those pools, mated, laid their eggs and went away. The eggs hatched and the tadpoles grew as the ponds shrank. The ponds were dried up by June, but by then enough of the toad tadpoles had grown into small toads to maintain a minor toad population even in that inhospitable area.

In point of evolution, the salamanders are the closest of the amphibians to the mammals and all the land animals that came after the first amphibian. But salamanders, as we know them, never evolved far as a species. The biggest achievement, it seems to me, was the salamander's method of achieving live birth. At mating time the male salamander deposits a conical mass of jellylike substance on which, or in which, is the sperm. The female draws this mass of sperm-bearing jelly into herself and there it fertilizes her eggs. The eggs hatch and she bears live young.

This is an advance over the somewhat random fertilization of most fish eggs. Frogs never achieved it. But some fish did. So there we have a crude form of live birth and a beginning of the mating and birthing of the mammal. Neither fish nor salamander, however, achieved the next phase of mammalian motherhood, mammary glands and nipples at which the young are fed directly from the mother. That was a long step forward, and the slow-moving salamander never achieved it.

The earliest amphibians appeared on earth about 350 million years ago, in what the geologists know as the Devonian period. They throve for at least fifty million years, perhaps as long as a hundred million, all through the Carboniferous period, the Coal Age, when the giant tree ferns covered the land and laid down the materials for our coal beds.

Undoubtedly there were many kinds of primitive amphibians, and they must have been of various shapes and sizes. We know the very earliest of them only by five-toed footprints they left in the sandy mud of the seashore, later consolidated into stone. Those five toes are a point to remember when we look at our own hands and feet, for we, too, are five-toed creatures.

Some of those early amphibians probably were insect eaters, since insects became numerous for the first time during their age of ascendancy. Nature wouldn't have overlooked that source of food. And some of them undoubtedly were carnivorous, living on others of their own kind. Most of them, though, must have been plant eaters, since the land was then overrun with plant life and there is a tendency of all life to eat that which is most abundant in its habitat.

We have clues to the later amphibians—and by later I mean those of the Coal Age—because fossil remains of them have been found. Some had heads as big as those of today's donkeys. Some had vocal cords and could make sounds in their throats, as frogs and toads do. Some lacked vocal cords and were silent, as are today's salamanders. All of them must have had true lungs, or at the least transitional lungs, so they could live on land in the open air. But all of them had to return to the water to mate and lay eggs; their young had to begin life as aquatic creatures.

We can speculate about those early amphibians on a basis of knowledge of those least removed from them today, the salamander and the newt. Some of them, at least, had the power of regrowth. The newts of today still have it. If a newt loses a leg, or even an eye, it can grow a new one. Sometimes the replacement is deformed, but it is a new member just the same, regenerated by the body, and it serves a purpose. This power of regrowth has come down to various of today's creatures, though sometimes in a restricted way. Most lizards can regenerate a lost tail, though the new tail often is misshapen or shorter than the original one. A snail can replace a lost horn, even to the eye at its tip. A crab can replace a claw, though the new one usually is smaller than the one lost. Many worms can regenerate themselves if a major portion is left to start the process.

Man has this ability to a limited extent. If I lose a patch of skin by burn or abrasion, I can replace it. My body will grow new skin, though it may leave a scar to mark the spot. If I break a bone, it will grow back together. If I tear off a fingernail, it will grow back. I cannot regenerate a finger or an arm, however. I have evolved beyond that point. Why? Probably because my body has grown so complex, and possibly because I am supposed to be clever enough and wise enough to take sensible care of myself. Nature seems to look after her own only up to a certain point; beyond that they are supposed to fend for themselves.

The frogs along my river cannot replace a lost leg. They, too, grew beyond that stage of self-replacement. But their tadpoles still can. If a fish nips off the tail of a tadpole, that tadpole simply grows a new tail. If it loses a leg, it grows a new leg. Once

185

it leaves the tadpole stage, however, it loses this replacement power. It has quick eyesight and it has vigorous legs, and if it cannot save itself from natural enemies then it must perish. Nature went so far with it, gave it the equipment to become a mature frog, and then left it to its own devices.

The frog—and its cousin the toad—has done very well with its own equipment. Fossil frogs and toads have been found in rocks fifty or sixty million years old, and those ancient frogs seem to be almost identical with the frogs and toads of today. Fossils of frogs with tails have been found in rocks 200 million years old. Except for the presence of tails, these frogs were not greatly different from those of the later periods. In all that time, 150 million years or so, evolution did little to the frog except remove his tail, which must have been an invitation to his enemies and, by all the purposes of logic, should have been sacrificed much sooner than it was. But nature and the slow processes of evolution move at their own pace.

Other changes did occur, over the eons. There is today a tropical frog that spends much of its time in the treetops. Its feet are not only webbed but the toes are very long and the webs very wide. By spreading these broad fan-webbed feet this frog can launch itself from a treetop and glide like a flying squirrel. It is called a "flying frog," though the name is in error. It cannot fly, but it can glide remarkable distances.

There are other exotic frogs that lay their eggs in cup-shaped leaves, where the tadpoles grow in pools of dew or rain. There are frogs that blow a mass of wet bubbles and hatch their eggs in that. There are toads that hatch their eggs in their mouths. There are even toads that hatch eggs in big pores on their own backs. The variants are many.

One of the simpler but still remarkable adaptations is that of the spring peeper, the hyla that makes the lowlands just down the road from my house loud with sound on mild Spring evenings. This small tree frog has long toes tipped with sticky, round pads that enable it not only to climb trees but to cling to surfaces as smooth as glass.

One Spring evening I heard a peeper calling almost at my elbow as I sat in the living room. I went out on the porch and searched every inch of it, I thought. Then I looked on the trees and bushes nearby, remembering that the peeper sometimes has an almost ventriloquistic ability. Not a sign of a hyla, which had been silent all the time I was looking. I returned to my chair, and within two minutes he was calling again, still there at my elbow. And at last I saw him, in the center of a window-pane within three feet of my chair.

How or why he came there, I have no idea. Hylas often call from across the river but I had never before heard one within a quarter of a mile of the house. But there he was, and there he remained for an hour. I had a good look at him through the glass, saw how he puffed and made his trilling call. And I had a close-up look at those pads at the end of his toes. They were like small foam-rubber buttons, and they were so effective that he shifted his position several times on that polished glass without losing his grip. He sat as firmly as though he were perched on sandpaper. He seemed as sure-footed as a fly.

I watched that hyla and I listened to him, and I silently thanked him and his kind, including the newts and the sala-manders, for three things the amphibians contributed to me and all my mammalian kind. For lungs, with which I can breathe the open air and live on the dry land of this earth. For vocal cords—the newts and the salamanders got no credit there, however—with which I can use the air in my lungs to speak my thoughts or sing my songs and communicate with my mate and all the others around me. And for legs on which to walk and run and fingers with which to manipulate the tools of my life's routine.

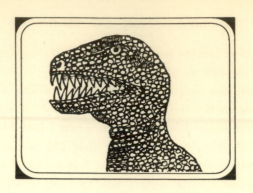

Reptiles

The Terrible Lizards

About 300 million years ago, as man reckons time, an amphibian found a way to hatch its eggs on land and eliminated the necessity of ever returning to the water. In our terms, that was the first reptile, and the event ushered in an age dominated by the dinosaurs, a word from the Greek terms for "terrible lizards." That age continued for perhaps 150 million years. During a considerable part of that time the reptiles, some of them the largest land animals of which we have any record, populated and ruled over the land. But somewhere along the way one of those reptiles, probably a relatively small one, grew a membrane between its legs, learned first to glide and then to fly. Another, which already had found it expedient to hatch its eggs inside its own body, enlarged an oil gland and began secreting from it a fluid with which to feed its young. Thus came about the beginnings of birds and mammals. Thus approached the twilight of the Age of Reptiles and the dawn of the Age of Mammals.

It wasn't quite as simple as it sounds. Nothing in nature is as simple as it sometimes seems when reduced to words. Evolution is not a straight-line process, like industrial manufacturing. If it were, the old models would be discontinued entirely and only the very newest ones would be made. If that were true in nature, creatures without backbones would have vanished when vertebrates evolved, fish would have vanished when amphibians evolved, amphibians would have vanished when reptiles came along, and reptiles would have vanished when birds and mammals came along. But nature doesn't work that way. Life diverges, evolves in many directions, but many of the old forms persist.

No one can say with certainty how many forms of life there have been or how or why some of them vanished. Our best reference file of the past is in the fossil beds, but even that is sketchy and incomplete. It is more like the contents of a few wastebaskets than a library of chronological data. There are gaps in the record that we can bridge only by guesswork and deduction. We constantly have to fall back on living antiques— reptiles, for instance—for confirmation of our guesswork. Out of fossils and living antiques and informed guesswork we have built what knowledge we have of the way life on this planet evolved and developed.

Change, as far back as we can see or envision, has been continuous. But nowhere along the way did basic life forms vanish completely. They elaborated, or they varied, or they diverged, but while nature was creating countless variants and multiplying life endlessly, some of the old forms persisted. So, although they are mere remnants of a kind that dominated the world for millions of years before they were superseded, snakes, lizards, alligators and turtles still persist. The reptilian way of life was successful enough, in a few forms, to outlive the eons.

I could do without some of today's reptiles, but nature couldn't. They still fill a niche in nature's economy, and they represent a stage of evolution that apparently was indispensable in the long history of life. Moreover, they may be, like other forms of life that we consider antique, kept here on the reserve shelf of nature just in case they are ever needed again for some evolutionary purpose man cannot imagine.

Man thinks of himself as the peak of evolution, and from the human point of view he is—up to this point. But that doesn't mean that the whole evolutionary urge, the driving compulsion of change, has now come to a halt. It may mean just the opposite. The whole process of evolutionary change seems to have speeded up over the past hundred million years or so. And in some ways nature's economy is economical beyond belief; nature seems always to have the parts and the materials at hand when they are needed for some job of rebuilding or remodeling. I am confident that if it should become necessary to revert a few eons and start evolving life all over again, somewhere in the infinity of nature there would be the materials with which to do it. I am not fond of the reptiles, but there might be a less promising place to start than with them. Theirs was a tremendously exciting age with a wealth of possibilities.

My prejudice against reptiles is unreasonable and largely confined to snakes. It comes from my boyhood, which was spent in a country that abounded with snakes, rattlesnakes among them. I saw a man die of rattlesnake bite, and I saw horses and cattle die of it, and I cannot forget. I later learned to grant all snakes, even poisonous ones, a proper place in the big biological picture, but those early emotions persist. Reason is a weak weapon against them.

There are few snakes in the valley where I now live. The river has its water snakes, there is an occasional garter snake in the yard or the garden, and in the pastures and woods I see a blacksnake now and then. They and I live in a tolerant state of truce, for I know they do little harm and much good. The rocky ledges of my mountainside are typical copperhead habitat, but I have never found one there. For that I am grateful, for I have no truce with copperheads.

Turtles are in another category. There are hundreds of turtles on the river, yellow-bellied sliders, painted turtles, small spotted turtles, and wood turtles along the banks. And there are snapping turtles, for which I have no enmity but complete respect. Now and then we hook one while fishing and haul it to the surface, where it and we exchange baleful glares. Then if it does not snap the hook I cut the line, and it goes its truculent way.

Last summer I saw a big snapper and a five-foot water snake in an hour-long battle in a marsh at the mouth of one of the brooks. How the snapper got a hold on the snake in the first place I do not know, but when I first sighted them the snake was caught in those fierce, wire-cutter jaws, only the front two thirds of its body free.

It was a hopeless fight. The snake had no weapons but its constricting coils and the battering but fangless blows it could deal with its head. The snapper was not only armed, mouth and claw, but it was armored with its heavy shell. The snake hammered at the snapper's head and neck, striking repeatedly with no effect. It threw a coil of its body around the snapper's shell, tightened till its muscles corded, and the snapper merely braced its feet. With a twist, the snake flipped the turtle onto its back. The turtle's hind feet reached and raked with vicious claws, and the snake's hold loosened. The turtle scrambled to its feet again.

Half a dozen times the snake looped and squeezed, with no effect at all. The turtle kept shifting its hold, each new bite taking more of the snake's vitality. Finally the snake swung a body loop toward the turtle's neck, its one chance of victory. Had it been able to catch that neck, the battle would have been over, probably a Pyrrhic victory, for the snake was seriously hurt. But it failed. The turtle, snapping with amazing speed, caught the snake just behind the head. That settled it, though the snake flipped the turtle over twice more and thrashed desperately. At last it began to relax, the relaxation of defeat and death.

What I watched, there in the reedy marsh, was a modern miniature, even to the setting, of the kind of battles to death that must have occurred 100 million years and more ago. Such battles were also fought between reptiles, because there were no other major combatants on the land anywhere.

The number and variety of the reptiles during the thousands of centuries that they dominated land life was amazing. It was as though animal life had exploded into a multitude of forms. We don't know why this happened, but it was during a geologic time when most of the land was low-lying and wet, when the climate was mild and humid, and when vegetation was so lush as to be extravagant. The jungles of tree ferns apparently were dying out, but other plants came spreading after them in profusion. It was after the extensive glaciation of the Southern Hemisphere and before the massed glaciers moved down from the north. It must have been a fertile time for life, all life. Toward the end of the period the great mountain chains were rising and vast deserts came into being; but by then the big lizards had reached their peak in size and the first small mammals were beginning to get a foothold.

The smallest of the reptilian creatures were not much bigger than sparrows, but the biggest of them were almost ninety feet long, stood close to twenty-five feet high and must have weighed about thirty-five tons. Some were lizards much like those we know today. Some were like today's alligators and crocodiles. Some were something like today's rhinoceroses, armored in huge scaly plates and armed with three long horns in a row on their snouts. Some were like huge, grotesque kangaroos with scaly legs and three-toed chicken-feet and ponderous tails fifteen feet long. There were even fishlike ichthyosaurs with bodies somewhat like whales and legs reduced to paddles. There were water-dwelling plesiosaurs fifty feet long, with necks and heads like snakes and legs like oars. These had reverted to the earlier element, water, which their ancestors had deserted; but they, too, were reptilian and had the basic characteristics of their land-dwelling kin.

There were light-boned pterodactyls, with heads like alligators, bodies like bats, tails like long whips with tufted ends. They grew membranes that they could spread into wings. Some of them had a twenty-four-foot wingspread; some were smaller than robins.

But there was a basic flaw in most of these reptiles, especially the giants. Their bodies grew to tremendous size but their brains remained almost rudimentary. The Triceratops, a rhinoceroslike creature that weighed at least ten tons, had a brain that weighed no more than two pounds. And the Stegosaurus, a thirty-foot lizard with a row of big vertical plates like a dorsal fin, had a brain estimated at two and a half ounces, about the size and weight of one of the small dry-cell batteries that power my flashlight. Some kangaroolike lizards that stood twenty feet high had nerve centers over their hips that were larger than the brains in their skulls.

It was a fantastic world, an unbelievable age. Reconstructing it now, it seems astonishing that with all its possibilities for life, the forms of that life appear to have been largely limited to reptiles. Life proliferated, it overran the land, it diverged in form a thousand ways. But apparently the cold-blooded, egg-laying basic species dominated until relatively late. With all this variety of life, one expects basic changes more extensive than seem to have occurred. Yet out of this age came the vast variety of life we know today.

There is temptation to say that this intense fecundity and this persistent trend toward giantism in the lizards was a result

193

of what we would call a favorable climate for growth. But that does not explain everything. Plentiful food encourages both size and numbers. But why did the bodies of so many of those swarming giants outrace their brains? An abundance of food made life easy, but a corresponding abundance of animal life created competitive conditions of life. Brain power would not have been totally wasted even in that environment so favorable to physical prosperity.

Life was a struggle, even in that Eden, a battle for existence. An eighty-foot-long plant eater might easily find its necessary quarter of a ton of green food every day, but if it hadn't the wit to avoid attack by a twenty-foot, sharp-toothed carnivorous neighbor the plenitude of food was of no importance. It died in the midst of plenty, and even more quickly than it would have starved to death in a desert. And the carnivores ate each other. The world must have roared continuously with the battles of the titans. But both the giant vegetarians and the giant flesh eaters eventually vanished. It was the lesser members of the tribe that persisted; and the remnants of those lesser ones still survive. The largest of them are the alligators and crocodiles and big turtles, all of them pygmies compared with the masters of the Age of Lizards.

Why did they vanish? There are various theories.

Some think that the cooling climate and the drying up of vast marshlands did them in. This supposes that they had little adaptability, which seems likely in animals with scant brain capacity. Yet how much brain, even relatively, has an ant or a bee or a wasp or a dragonfly? They were here before the big lizards; they have survived countless climatic and geologic changes.

Some believe that the early mammals, creatures perhaps the size of today's rats, ate the reptiles' eggs. This, too, has an air of plausibility, since most of the big lizards were egg-layers. But there were a great many lizards and there must have been a great many eggs. This theory presupposes a big population of egg-eating mammals, each with a huge appetite.

Some believe that they were simply outdated, that change was overdue, that the lizards, particularly the giants, had already outstayed their time. This has overtones of a belief in cyclic change, but it is not in itself persuasive. It takes little account of basic weaknesses in the species.

Whatever the theory, the fact is that the big lizards vanished. They vanished rather quickly, in terms of geologic time, after they reached their physical peak. With our customary excellence of hindsight, we can say that as a species they had fundamental shortcomings or that they abandoned certain fundamental necessities for survival.

First, they outgrew their own brains. No creature with more brain power in its hind legs than it has in its head has the wit to survive in a competitive world.

Second, their reproductive system was inadequate. We have no means of knowing how many eggs a prehistoric lizard laid, but it seems unlikely that a dinosaur, particularly a big one, ever laid as many as a sunfish or a frog. To survive, an egg-layer must give enough hostages to the hazardous conditions of the hatch to insure at least two adult and reproducing offspring. And there probably was little parental care, if any. Reptiles seldom care for their young even as casually as some fish. The surviving reptiles give their young almost no care after hatching. Most of them, however, even the turtles and the alligators, lay many eggs at one time. Perhaps that is one reason they survived, for they gave their kind at least a mathematical chance.

Third, the big lizards were what we call cold-blooded. They lived at approximately the same temperature as the surrounding air, and in cool weather their whole life process slowed down. Many of them were too big to burrow into the mud and hibernate, as snakes, lizards and turtles do today. They were particularly at the mercy of climatic change, and one winter such as we now have in New England would have killed them by the tens of thousands. There is some evidence that toward the close of their era some of the pterodactyls, the pre-birds, did begin to warm their own blood, move over toward the warm-blooded species of today.

And finally, although they branched out in all directions—or perhaps because of that—they specialized fatally. This is obvious from their fossil remains. They were physically unable to accept change, even such minor change as the alteration of a few types of vegetation. And, like most highly specialized animals of today, they may have been more than usually susceptible to disease. Disease seems often to take violent and fatal hold when any creatures overcrowd their environment.

It is even conceivable that natural radiation was a factor in their extinction, as it is possible that excessive radiation had something to do with their origin and their frequently fantastic physical forms. We do not yet know enough about the mutation effects of radiation to make more than the most speculative guesses about what it may have done in the remote past.

But while they were here—and remember that the lizards, large and small, and all the other ancient reptiles dominated land life for about 150 million years—they developed certain characteristics that have marked or have been of enduring effect on most of the animal life that came after them. I am what I am at least in part because of what the ancient reptiles were, and so is my dog, so are the cows whose milk I drink, so are the birds that make my mornings sing.

Basic to the change from amphibian to reptile was the development of a dry skin that protects the body from excessive evaporation. Amphibians died if their skin became dry. The skin of reptiles conserved the body's moisture. My skin conserves my inner moisture, releasing just enough to cool the skin by evaporation in intense heat. The reptile's skin was usually covered with some form of horny scales or plates, but in later stages some of those scales began evolving toward feathers and others toward hair. But in all of them there was freedom, at last, from the porous, naked skin that kept amphibians close to water.

The amphibians had developed legs strong enough to support their bodies without the help of surrounding water. The reptiles developed those legs into sturdy limbs for running, leaping and fighting. They were usually four-legged, with clawed toes on their feet, but some of them traveled on two legs. And others developed the legs and toes into wing frames for flight.

Reptiles produced eggs that would hatch on land. These eggs were larger than those of fish and amphibians, they contained a generous food supply for the hatching fetus, and they had inner membranes and protective outer shells. Some of them, undoubtedly the smaller, physically lesser ones, developed a system of live birth; the mother retained the fertilized eggs inside until they hatched.

This was not new with the reptiles. It was a transition stage —an experiment, perhaps—which some fish and some amphibians had already achieved. But it was a fundamental step in the change from the free-egg system toward placental birth, which is typical of the mammal. It is unlikely that any of the reptiles progressed to the point where an oil gland in the skin enlarged and began secreting mother-manufactured food for the young. That was the next step, development of the mammary glands. But in all reptiles, whether they laid eggs or had some transitional form of live birth, the eggs were fertilized inside the female by injection of sperm by the male. The haphazard fertilization of the eggs externally, common in fish and amphibians, was being superseded.

The lines of change are not at all clear and we have no calendar for them. We speak of the process as evolution, which literally means a rolling out, or an unrolling. The scope of life was broadening and becoming more complex. We think of ourselves as the apex of that evolution, which is understandable since we are the ones who pass the judgment. But I am not prepared to say that the whole course of evolution was aimed at the eventual development of man. It may have been. Man has a degree of awareness and a capacity for life that apparently are unmatched. But why did vestiges of every stage of evolution that we can trace persist? Single-celled organisms persist. So do primitive multiple-celled plants and animals, even those so ambiguous that we cannot say of certainty that they are plant *or* animal. Fish persist, even very primitive ones, and so do salamanders and lizards. And so do insects, which are a source of knotty questions every time one ventures down this road of speculation.

If the whole evolutionary process was devoted to the creation of man, where do all these other forms of life fit in? I cannot say that they were created only for man's use or to make this a more habitable, a prettier, or a more enjoyable place to live in. I keep wondering if they haven't their own place and purpose in the order of life, and if they wouldn't have had that place even if I had never been here to be aware of them.

The reptiles dominated the world for about 150 million years. Most of them vanished when mammals and birds became numerous. The mammals have dominated the scene for only about 100 million years, and man has been here less than one million years. Perhaps we should wait a few thousand more years before we speak of the giant lizards as an experiment in evolution that turned out to be a failure.

The blacksnake on my mountainside and the turtle in my river do not speak a language I can understand. They have nowhere near the brain capacity I have. I cannot grant them much intelligence, nor any imagination, love or compassion. I am sure their powers of memory are limited. But they are here today, and their presence proves that the reptile, for all its cold blood, its oviparous birth and its limited brain power, is a persistent and successful form of life. In its own way, that life has adapted to far more change than man has ever known. I can only hope that my own kind has as much persistence, as a species, as those reptilian neighbors of mine have.

Birds

A Feather, a Wing and a Song

WHEN a whippoorwill wakens me at three-thirty in the morning, I try to be philosophical about it. I tell myself that the whippoorwill is a nocturnal bird that says goodnight just before dawn. But why, my human brain demands, must he say his matutinal goodnight so loudly, so monotonously and so repetitiously? And when a brown thrasher begins to sing just as I am getting back to sleep it does no good at all to tell myself that the thrasher is an early riser. If I get back to sleep, I am certain to be wakened by five by the whole chorus, robins, orioles, tanagers, house wrens, with the background of mourning doves, crows and jays. Why? Because one of the birds' inalienable rights, one of their finest evidences that they are no longer reptiles, is their power of song.

All birds had reptilian ancestors. So did I; so we are, in a sense, distant cousins. But the birds long ago learned the art of flight and clothed themselves with feathers, though they continued, like reptiles, to reproduce by laying eggs. My kind became bipedal mammals with dextrous hands instead of wings, and with no feathers.

Nobody knows why one branch of the reptile tribe long ago became birds and another branch became mammals. Something happened, and it cannot wholly be explained by any theory of natural selection. Selection helped, after the commitment was made, the direction of change chosen. But before selection came strongly into play there was the basic divergence from the reptilian form and way of life. And that divergence, significantly in both instances, bird and mammal, was in the direction of more brain power. The bigger, more effective brain was of more enduring importance than wings or manual dexterity or placental birth.

The oldest known bird is a fossil preserved in stone that the paleontologists say was laid down in the Jurassic period, about 150 million years ago. In some ways that fossil bird resembles the parent reptiles. It has teeth in both jaws, it has a long, lizard-like tail, and it has other, lesser lizard characteristics. But it has recognizable wings, it has abdominal ribs and a breastbone, both of which reptiles lack. By every anatomical test it is a bird, but a bird still in transition from one group to the other.

Details of evolutionary change are not always obvious until the change is more or less complete. We have to guess at many intermediate steps, and some of those steps are vitally important yet completely mysterious. For instance, the change from cold-bloodedness to warm-bloodedness was a basic alteration, yet we have no evidence of how or when it began. The reptiles were and still are cold-blooded, dependent on the temperature of their environment. Mammals and birds are warm-blooded, relatively independent of environmental temperature.

We speak of this change as high achievement and we sometimes think that it enabled birds and mammals to move freely about the earth. We sometimes say that it provides warm-blooded animals with more energy than cold-bloodedness. But when we make such statements we overlook the insects— again! Insects are cold-blooded, but they are numerous beyond counting and they live almost everywhere. And insects have more energy per ounce than any other creatures alive. I have also heard it said that warm-bloodedness enables its possessors to live longer, more active lives. Again, the insects defeat at least half of that statement. Some insects live, in the larval stage, for years. The larvae of the periodic locust, for instance, live much longer than most small, warm-blooded mammals and even longer than most birds. Insects are slowed down by cold weather, and warm-blooded creatures continue active, generally speaking. There are a few warm-blooded hibernators, such as bears and woodchucks, but virtually all insects hibernate in some form.

I should say that the biggest advantage of warm-bloodedness is that it produces nervous energy. Nervous energy is basic to intelligence, to thought. No one has yet discovered much brain power in any cold-blooded creatures, perhaps because of that very lack of nervous energy. Most of the cold-blooded ones, including both insects and reptiles, are dependent on instinct and reflex rather than intelligence. Instinct does not require thought or much nervous energy, and it does not require a brain of any consequence. A few ganglia or nerve centers suffice to prompt the muscles and the reflexes.

The big changes from reptilian life to avian life can be stated rather simply. First was the development of a heart that supplies the body with pure blood, blood already circulated through the lungs and supplied with oxygen. The cold-blooded reptiles circulate mixed blood, blood only partly purified in the lungs. So the first major change was in the heart, which in birds pumps impure blood to the lungs, purifies and aerates it, and sends only such purified blood to the rest of the body. This promotes energy.

The second major change was to warm-bloodedness, important for activity around the clock, both the clock of the day and that of the year. But this change is still incomplete in birds. In many species the nestlings are cold-blooded at the time of hatching and will soon die if not warmed by the mother for the first few days, until their own heat-regulating system is established—their warm-bloodedness.

The third change was the development of feathers. Feathers apparently are an elaboration of scales, common to reptiles. Birds have scales on their legs and feet, often on their beaks, but feathers elsewhere on their bodies. Nobody knows how the feather evolved, but the feather as we know it today is a remarkable achievement with many different forms, from fluffy, insulating down to tough protective outer feathers, to strong, movable wing feathers for flight. Feathers protect the bird's body, streamline it for flight, and provide the completed wing for flight. The bird's wing is very different from that of the bat, for instance, and different from that of the ancient "flying dragon," in both of which the flight foil was a stretched membrane.

The fourth change was in the bird's skeleton. Most of the ancient lizards had heavy bones. The bird's bones are hollow and light in weight, with tubular strength. And the whole skeleton of a bird is designed for muscular strength to drive the wings.

Finally, and in some ways most important of all, the birds achieved bigger brains, relatively, than any of their ancestors. Along with these brains came acute senses, particularly vision and, in many instances, hearing.

Birds have evolved in a great variety of sizes and specialized forms. The ruby-throated hummingbird is only three and a quarter inches long and without its feathers is not much bigger than a bumblebee. There is an even smaller variety native to Cuba. At the other extreme, the albatross may have a wing span of twelve feet or more and the California vulture has a spread of wings sometimes reaching eleven feet. And birds vary from the flightless penguins and ostriches to the swallows and nighthawks, which are far more at home in the air than on the ground. Here in my small valley the native birds vary from the stilt-legged herons to the miniature hummingbirds, from the stub-winged kingfishers to the graceful sparrow hawks, from deep-diving mergansers to water-hating crows. There are ruffed grouse in the woods, and there are jeering catbirds in the forsythia bushes, long-billed house wrens and short-billed purple finches, hook-beaked owls and chisel-beaked pileated woodpeckers.

In almost all birds, the power of vision is excellent. It is highly specialized in some, however. The kingfisher, for example, has a kind of double vision, one type for seeing in the air, the other for seeing under water; both are combined in the same pair of eyes, and both are acute, thoroughly efficient. Some insects have acute vision, but it is limited in range. The ant, for example, can see clearly only about three feet and has only about six feet of useful vision. Yet vision is probably the most efficient of all insect senses except possibly the sense of touch.

The bird's eye, like my own and those of all vertebrate animals, is essentially a sphere of transparent membrane filled with fluid. This creates a lens that transmits the image to the optic nerves. Insects and other backboneless animals have compound eyes, a series of small lenses formed from layers of the skin, which focus light on sensitive nerve cells but do not produce any single clear image. Each lens is in effect a single eye, and the creature sees a whole series of somewhat blurred images.

The large, single-lens eye is not new with the birds, but its high development is. And that development is a part of the whole brain development. This also is shown in the acute sense of hearing in birds. But few birds have much of a sense of smell or taste. Nor is there any strong sense of touch, generally, among the birds. They have no antennae, like insects, or fingers, like men; and antennae and fingers are peculiarly sensitive to touch.

In most reptiles the brain is very small in relation to the size of the animal, small even in proportion to the size of the skull. In birds it is large. The old epithet "bird-brained" has no basic truth; a bird's brain is small only in comparison with the brain of a man, not in relation to the bird's own body. And it is this development of the brain, and all its capacities, that baffles the evolutionists. Nobody knows why the bird family and the mammal family diverged from the original reptile stock, and nobody knows how the brain grew or exactly why.

But along with this brain growth, perhaps because of it, the birds and mammals developed in their own ways and degrees a whole series of impulses and mental capacities that were unknown in the reptiles. The insects evolved a few parallel instincts, but never achieved true capacity for thought.

Birds have social impulses. They gather in flocks, somewhat as bees gather in swarms, and cliff swallows, for example, live in communities. But even these community-dwelling birds have almost no resemblance to ants or bees, since they have no community organization or division of labor. They remain individuals, pairing off only for mating and reproduction, and they care for the young as individuals, not as a community. Many birds pair and mate for the whole season, some for life. Geese show a kind of loyalty to the flock, and they show intense loyalty and even affection toward their own mates and their offspring.

Family care is habitual among most birds. One or the other of a pair broods the eggs in the nest, and often both parents feed the nestlings. The male is vigorous in his defense of the nest. A pair of kingbirds nest each year in a tree that overhangs the river just below my house, and when they are nesting the male is so truculently vigilant that he will make a noisy token attack on me every time I go near that tree in my boat. If a crow comes within fifty yards of the nest, this kingbird is off, screaming for reinforcements, to attack the crow; and always he puts the crow to rout, alone or with any volunteer allies who answer his alarm.

Care of the young is constant and sometimes almost hysterical. A pair of house wrens hatched a brood in a nest on one of the lower limbs of the big Norway spruce beside my house. I never saw more energy spent in parental care. Then two of the fledglings fluttered from the nest into the grass beneath, more eager than able to fly. The parents raised an uproar. When I went to see the cause they threatened to attack me. Their noise attracted three robins and a catbird, all of whom were ready to pitch into me. It was a kind of community crisis. The two fledglings finally hopped to safety in a bed of evening primroses in the flower garden, and I retired to watch. The parent birds spent the whole day fluttering from their remaining nest-bound chick to the two prodigals, watching for danger, burning up I don't know how much energy. The grounded chicks spent the night among the primroses, and the next day the vigil was resumed. It wasn't until the third day that they were able to get somewhat uncertainly into the air on short flights. The parents supervised those flights, and eventually the fledglings found apparent safety in a patch of sumac beside the river, able by then to fly twenty or thirty yards at a time.

But this I noticed: When those fledglings first fluttered from the nest and I went near them, the parents were frantic. By the second day they were apprehensive but less than frantic at my appearance. By the second evening I could crouch beside the fledglings without an uproar from the parents. They chattered apprehensively, but that was all. They had learned that I was not a predatory enemy. They did not come and perch on my shoulder and twitter a request that I shelter and protect their young ones, but they no longer tried to drive me away. They learned something. They had the brain capacity to learn from experience.

And that is true of all birds. Some learn more swiftly than others, but all of them seem able to appraise a situation and act with something approaching reason rather than with unreasoning instinct. Even a barnyard hen will learn a few lessons, if the teacher is persistent and if the lessons are simple. Chicks learn more swiftly than grown hens. And wild birds undoubtedly learn more quickly than domesticated ones. Domestication often leads to a slowing down of the ability to learn from experience, probably because the domesticated creature has little need to face the unexpected situation that calls for either swift learning or quick, decisive action. Given the brain capacity to learn, most animals learn from the necessity to learn, from demanding circumstances of life.

Almost all birds have a degree of structural ability. They build nests, and they sometimes build them with remarkable skill, when we consider how limited are their tools. They have nothing but their beaks and their feet to work with, and there is little dexterity in the feet, which are designed for scratching, for perching, or for capturing and tearing food. Yet the orioles build complicated nests, woven of hair and fibers, nests of considerable strength and flexibility which resist both wind and rain. Their weaving is irregular but sufficient for the purpose. And the simple fact that a pair of orioles can construct such a nest at all is marvelous to me.

Barn swallows regularly build their mud nests in my garage. They are not beautiful nests, but they are striking examples of bird patience and industry. The mud, in this instance a rather sandy mud from the riverbank, is brought, beakful by beakful, and plastered on one of the beams. The beams are rough, but I should have difficulty making such material stick to them. Yet the swallows build nests there that weigh two pounds, sandy mud with only an occasional short strand of grass in it and those strands probably accidental. They waste a little mud in their building, often dropping it on my car, which I do not appreciate. But for the most part their building is more efficient in terms of material than is the work of most human bricklayers.

English sparrows make jumbled nests of twigs and grass, in only the broadest sense structures; the nests are almost as messy as the birds themselves. A house wren's nest is in a heap of twigs, but it does have some shape and order. A hummingbird's nest is like a gem, the size of half an English walnut, a cup usually camouflaged on the outside with moss or lichen and lined inside with silky down from the mother bird's own breast. The two white eggs, incidentally, are not much larger than common garden peas.

This nesting is a part of the strongly developed parental instinct that is so outstanding among the birds. Some, of course, lack it. Cuckoos, for instance, and cowbirds lay eggs in other birds' nests and shirk parental responsibility. But all animals have their renegades. Nighthawks and whippoorwills build only the most rudimentary of nests, or none at all. Their beaks are not designed for such skills and their legs and feet are of only elementary use, for standing and shifting awkwardly about, and wholly unfit for nest building. They do care for their young with diligence. The whippoorwills even teach their fledglings the tribal calls.

Such "manual" skills as birds have are wholly utilitarian and there is little doubt that they are basically instinctive. No parent bird ever supervises the building of its yearling chick's first nest. The bird *knows* how to build a nest, doesn't have to learn. But in that building, birds do demonstrate a degree of flexibility in choosing among available materials. Orioles once used many strands of horsehair in weaving their nests. When horses became less numerous the orioles used less hair and more string and plant fiber. I examined an oriole nest a few months ago and found not one horsehair in it. Some insist that orioles prefer brightly colored string for their nests, but I doubt that. The orioles I have known have used scraps of any string available. They build for utility, not for show. So does the humming-bird, whose nest, beautiful as it is, is made to shelter eggs and nestlings, not as a work of art.

Birds have notable skills in flight and in song, and they are capable of using those skills to express what must be emotions. When we go out on the river in the boat on a Summer evening and the swallows gather there to feed, they often indulge in play. I can find no other explanation for their gyrations, their follow-the-leader tactics and their games of tag. I am sure they are not chasing insects when two or three of them, sometimes half a dozen, come sweeping toward the boat, usually in line, and spiral and climb and utter peeps that have every aspect of cries of pleasure. I have sat on the bank and watched them and seen no such maneuvers; then I have gone out in the boat and they have staged the aerial circus around the boat, as though showing off just for me. Perhaps I am interpreting too much, but if I am not actually an audience I am some kind of creature of which those swallows are aware and in front of which they play their games.

And I have watched, from indoors and out of sight, the play of blue jays in my apple trees. They, too, play tag, through the tangle of unpruned branches. And this happens in the Fall of the year, not at mating time. Mating and nesting by then are ended for the year. The jays are more self-conscious than the swallows. When I appear, the game ends abruptly. The jays perch, glare at me, put on their jeering pose, look solemnly at each other, then fly away. They play only in private.

And as for song, if birdsong were only a kind of elaborate mating call, why should the house wren be so full of song after the fledglings are hatched and gone? The wrens that nest regu-larly in my spruce are singing virtually all Summer, and their

July dawn singing is ecstatic. The same is true of the orioles who nest in my maples. They sing for song itself, or I am no judge of song. So does the brown thrasher who celebrates, morning after morning and evening after evening, from April till September. So does the wood thrush that makes the evenings throb with simple melody.

I am tempted to say that man learned song from the birds, that it expresses emotions that are common to both even if not quite comparable. But such a statement could be wholly wrong. It may be that the emotions prompted the song in both instances and independently. Perhaps it is best only to say that song is an expression of emotion in both birds and men. But that requires the statement that, of all animals, only birds and men have achieved both the emotions and the song to express them. Some mammals other than man, notably the dog and possibly the cat, express both joy and pain with a range of vocal sound, but they have never achieved the full ecstasy of song. We have diverged, the birds and my own kind, a long way from the emotional poverty and the oral limitations of the reptile tribe from which we sprang in the remote past.

The divergence of the birds was in one direction, that of my own kind in another. But both of us achieved new brain capacity, a broader range of emotions, some degree of reasoning power. And both of us achieved a degree of parental care for the young and of social impulses and needs that far outdistance the only approximation we know, that of the insects. The insect colony is almost entirely devoid of emotion, has virtually no capacity for thought or reason, and is devoted to continuation of the species. The birds have a limited social instinct or impulse, strong parental ties, a considerable capacity for learning, and a vigorous sense of the individual. And they have strong emotions. All these qualities link them in one way or another to that bipedal mammal who lacks feathers, man. We came down parallel roads from the emotional and intellectual caves of early reptilian life, and we have considerably more in common than the capacity for song. I am forever grateful that we both can sing, too, but most of all I am grateful that somewhere back there along the way the nodes of nerves in our craniums began to grow and complicate, began to evolve into brains that could wonder, and wish, and learn, and remember.

Mammals

The Story of a Brain

IT IS frequently said that this is the age of the mammals, that the mammals now dominate the earth. That is a fine, large statement, and in a sense it is undoubtedly true. But what of the insects? Those small, cold-blooded, chitin-clad bits of life crop up to pose gnarly questions almost every time one makes a big generalization. But I suppose one can say with a degree of certainty that mammals do now hold a kind of dominance. At least, we mammals assert our possession of the earth and one way or another we do keep the insects from overwhelming us. In that sense, this is the age of mammals. But it is a dubious distinction and the balance of power remains rather precarious.

The mammal is a comparatively old form of life. The earliest fossil mammals date from the Triassic period, about 190 million years ago, and most of the mammal families of today have fossil ancestors dating back at least sixty million years. The very early mammals were small, about the size of today's rats, and some of them were so tentatively mammalian that the paleontologists say they were distinctly reptilian in many characteristics. That is inevitable, since the mammals presumably sprang from reptilian stock.

Briefly stated, the mammal is an animal that usually has hair or fur, is warm-blooded, has four limbs, bears its young alive, and feeds its young from mammary glands in the mother.

There are exceptions, as there are in almost all families of animals. In the Australia–New Zealand zoo of primitives, for instance, is the platypus, which hatches its young from eggs laid in a nest. Yet the platypus is a mammal, fur-bearing, warm-blooded, four-legged and with mammary glands. There are no mammary teats, however; the milk oozes from pores in the skin and the young ones lick it off rather than suckling. Also in the Australian zoo is the echidna, the spiny anteater, which also lays eggs and has no teats on its mammary glands. And there are the marsupials—kangaroos and all the others whose young are born in a kind of larval stage and are nurtured at the mother's mammary teats inside an abdominal pouch. In the United States we have only one example of the marsupial family, the slow-witted opossum.

With the exception of the strange variants characteristic of the Australia–New Zealand area, the world's mammals are relatively obedient to the broad rules for their kind. But they are vastly varied, ranging in size from the tiny meadow vole to the whale, from the field mouse to the elephant. Some have horns on their heads. Many have hoofed feet. And all have teeth set in sockets in their jaws; among all the other animals, only the crocodiles have such teeth. And all mammals have a diaphragm, a sheet of muscle, across the body cavity separating the lungs and heart from the digestive organs.

In terms of physical equipment, the mammal is the most complex of all animals. Even the heart is complex, having four chambers to separate pure from impure blood and to circulate only pure, aerated blood to the body's vital organs and tissues. And all mammals have comparatively large and complex brains, relatively much larger and more complex than the brains of insects, fish, amphibians or reptiles.

Man speaks of the mammals as the highest achievement of evolution. By a stretch of the imagination I can conceive of the insects, if they were ever to consider such matters, believing that they, not the mammals, are the superior ones. In terms of brain power, however, there is little doubt that the mammal does stand at the top of the heap, with man at the very peak. But since we do not yet know the purpose of evolution, if indeed there is any purpose, such a classification may be somewhat arbitrary. If persistence of the species, for instance, were the criterion the insects would be among the logical applicants for high honors. The insects have been here, in much their present form, at least 200 million years, perhaps 250 million. Mammals have been here at most 190 million years. So we still have a few million years to go to prove that we have the endurance, as a species, that the insects have already demonstrated.

The very earliest mammals appeared at about the time the armored amphibians disappeared and the giant reptiles began to take over the scene. The mammals persisted, probably as very minor members of the teeming animal community, for close to 100 million years before they were ready to take command. Meanwhile, the giant reptiles, the dinosaurs and all their kind, rose and dominated the land, and began to decline.

The story of the mammals is misty and speculative during those early eons. Competition for living space and food was intense, and the process of natural selection inevitably came into play, as always in an uninhibited environment. Energy was needed to survive, great quantities of physical and nervous energy, and the trend toward warm-bloodedness undoubtedly provided that energy. This must have been accompanied by changes in the heart so that it could better circulate a greater quantity of fresh, aerated blood. And in such a busy, competitive society of animal life, those with the most alert senses and the most active brains had the best chance of survival. So the ones with the best brains were the ones that lived to reproduce.

Such a process is long and slow, but we are dealing now with a relatively long period of time, at least 100 million years, perhaps 150 million. It is difficult to understand why the same processes were not at work in the lizard family, but apparently they were not. For some reason, the lizards became larger and larger in body and their brains did not keep pace. They outgrew their own limited intelligence. And toward the end of that era, according to some theories, the mammals, insignificant though they were in size, undermined the whole structure of gigantic lizard life. The egg-laying lizards were almost entirely lacking in the instinct of parental care of the young. So, if the busy little mammals ate the eggs and the hatchlings of the big lizards, the end of the dinosaurian era was inevitable.

Granting the plausibility of these theories, other factors certainly were at work. The climate was changing. The food supply was diminishing for the big lizards. Many of them were vegetarians and needed several hundred pounds of food a day. As the food diminished, starvation threatened. The offspring of weakened parents must also have been weaklings. And as the vegetarians died off, the carnivorous lizards ran short of food. This could have been a disastrously vicious circle. Perhaps it was.

Also, the big lizards were not physically adaptable to a changing climate. We have limited evidence of this factor's effect in the fact that most of the lizards that have survived down to present times are those able to hibernate. One cannot imagine a dinosaur in hibernation the way a woodchuck, for instance, hibernates. In contrast, the warm-bloodedness of the mammals enabled them to adapt with relative ease to changes in climate.

Within a temperature range that would have fatally slowed down or killed the big, cold-blooded lizards, the mammals could continue to move about and live successfully.

Finally, there was the fact of live birth and parental care. The mammals seem early to have evolved a system of live birth, the eggs hatching inside a placental sac in the mother and being nourished and developed there, relatively safe from predators. This minimized the outside danger to the mammalian young in the egg and early-growth stages. And since the mammal also evolved glands in the female from which the young were fed on the mother's milk, parental care became characteristic of mammalian life. The family came into being. Among the egg-laying creatures, only the birds ever developed any degree of family consciousness. But here again one must make exception for the insects, especially the social insects, though theirs is communal rather than family care of the young.

In birds and mammals, however, the family was the foundation for the flock, the herd, the tribe, which evolved a sense of concerted effort toward a common purpose. If there were packs of hungry, primitive, ratlike mammals foraging together and raiding the rudimentary nests of the big lizards, the result was foredoomed. The mammals would eventually dominate the scene.

So much for theories and speculation. Toward the end of the period, when the big lizards were definitely on their way out, the mammals began to take over the dry land of this earth. And they by then had begun to diverge in a hundred different directions, to break up into many specialized families.

How these divergences came about is not known. I mention again the possibility of cosmic radiation and its effect on the genes of heredity. Certainly mutations appeared, and after the mutants came into being there again was the process of natural selection. Some of the variants were plant eaters. Some were flesh eaters. Some were omnivorous. Some burrowed into the ground for safety from their enemies. Some evolved long, agile legs and found safety in running away. Some grew fierce claws and fangs. Some took to the dry, arid wastelands. Some returned to the oceans. Some hid among the rocks. Some took to the tree-tops. And all of them used their wits, some more than others.

Conditions of climate and geography favored the mammal. Most of the modern continents were by then above water, most of the mountains we know today were already formed. And the climate was beginning to stabilize. Most of the modern plants were already in existence. The alternate advance and retreat of the big glaciers of relatively modern times had not yet begun. The world, in brief, was a hospitable place for the mammalian form of animal life.

So the mammals proliferated. The vast tribes of grass eaters, the deer, the bison, all the ancestors of our horses, cattle and sheep, multiplied and began to specialize. The carnivorous beasts, primarily of the cat and dog families, grew to large size and intense ferocity. The aquatic mammals, whales, seals, walruses and all their kind, occupied the waters of the earth and found there vast quantities of food. And the lesser ones, the rodents, the whole tribe of gnawing creatures who may have come directly from the very earliest mammals, filled the chinks in the living space—the mice, the rats, the squirrels, the beavers and all their kind.

Among themselves, the mammals multiplied prodigiously and spread over the earth, from the polar regions to the tropics, from the waters and the marshlands to the woods, the plains and the deserts. There are today about fifteen thousand species and subspecies of mammals grouped by the zoologists into 118 families. No one can say with certainty how many species of mammals have vanished over the past fifty or sixty million years, but some of them certainly evolved down dead-end alleys and are known only by fossil remains.

I have no notion of attempting here to follow in any detail

the evolution of the mammals. One typical example, the horse, can be briefly summarized. About sixty million years ago the horse was only about a foot high, a doglike creature with five toes on each foot. It was common here in the Americas. Nourished by lush grass, it grew in size, became as big as a collie dog. Its feet changed, perhaps to enhance its speed afoot. It became a three-toed animal. Then the two remaining outer toes diminished in function and finally became rudimentary and it walked on one toe, and the hoof of the modern horse evolved. For some reason still unknown, the prehistoric horse vanished in America about thirty thousand years ago and the wild horses of central Asia became the direct ancestors of today's horses. Of all the mammals we know today, the story of the horse's physical evolution is the most nearly complete in terms of paleontological evidence.

But the story of the mammals is essentially the story of a brain, not the story of any one family of animals. In all the creatures that preceded the mammal the brain was essentially a nerve center whose primary function was to run the relatively simple processes of the body. As vision and other senses improved, certain areas of the brain increased in size and efficiency to receive and transmit the messages these senses picked up. But most of the actions of the animal were a result of instinct, and the brain's function was limited. I mentioned earlier that some of the giant lizards had brains smaller than the nerve centers that dictated the motions of the hind legs. Insects developed more brain power, proportionate to their bodies, than any of the early animals; yet the insects never advanced much beyond the stage of instinctive action.

In the mammals, however, the brain began to grow and increase its capacity. Perhaps most important of all, it evolved a sense center that could take account of the messages delivered by eyes, ears, nose and tactile organs. This was new. It enabled the mammal to receive a complex message from several sense sources at once. Out of it eventually came the mental capacity to appraise such a complex message, not merely to set instinctive actions into motion.

Paleontologists and biologists can point to a whole series of changes in the brain. They can show how one area developed, then another, all leading toward full development of the best brain we know, that of man. It is a long and complex story, best told by the specialists; but involved in it are the factors of memory, of anticipation, and of reason. All three of these faculties are vital to intelligence. Lacking any one of them, the animal is forced to fall back on primitive instincts.

Why the brain should have grown and become more and more complex in the tribe of mammals that eventually led to man is one of those mysteries of evolution that may never be solved. Certain tree shrews, squirrellike animals of Java, show a line of evolution toward man, particularly in their brains. The tree-shrew's forebrain or cerebrum is developed beyond that of any primitive animal. The forebrain is where all the sense impressions are received and sorted out. It is also where orders originate for bodily response, especially what are called manipulative actions. Manipulative actions lead toward skill with the hands and the fingers.

These tree shrews indicate a brain development that was carried still further in the lemurs, the marmosets and the monkeys. Out of that phase of evolution, somewhere along the line, it is generally agreed that man's ancestors must have emerged. It is now largely accepted that the first men were not apes. They were variants in a common stock, and they evolved along their own path. There are some resemblances to man in the apes, but the ape tribe went their own way after the original diversion and apparently they never were even semihuman.

Much has been made, at one time and another, of man's anatomy in comparison with that of the ape, and especially of man's development of the opposed thumb. Many have insisted that the opposed thumb is responsible for man's manual skills and, in that sense, is responsible for man's evolution and his unique degree of dominance over his environment.

Perhaps so, but not even the opposed thumb could achieve a great deal in the way of skill without a brain to guide it. When I remember men who still had remarkable manual skills after the accidental loss of a thumb, or men who developed remarkable skills with two-fingered mechanical hands after they had lost their own hands, I am skeptical of such broad conclusions. I think of the ant and the bee, so instinctively skillful with no hands or fingers but only their mouths with which to work. And I think of the skill of the Baltimore oriole, weaving a nest with only its beak for a tool.

The human hand is a notably skillful member, but it only obeys the orders of the infinitely more skillful brain. The most adept hands in the world would be of limited use if they were guided only by unreasoning instinct. And the opposed thumb is no more than a fortunate circumstance. The brain is the dominant factor, the essential difference between the mammal and all its predecessors. I have only to look at my animal neighbors to find sufficient proof to satisfy me.

Among those neighbors are opossums and raccoons. Both are mammals, the opossum a marsupial. The opossum has a foot like a human hand, even to the opposed thumb which is especially noticeable on the hind foot. Yet the opossum is one of the most blundering, incompetent animals I know, slow-witted and so immature nervously that it literally falls into a faint, a kind of coma, at the sign of danger. It survives as a species largely because it is so prolific and has so few natural enemies.

The raccoon also has five agile toes on each foot, but it lacks the opposed thumb. Its fingers are so adept, however, and its brain is so clever, that it can open a cage latch with little hesitation, and it can even open simple padlocks after a few minutes of inspection and investigation. The raccoon uses those adept forefeet with more skill than most six-year-old children use their hands. The essential difference between the opossum and the raccoon is in the brain, not the toes. The raccoon is one of the most intelligent of all small animals, and the opossum is one of the most stupid.

But there are only a few low-scale mammals, like the opossum. Most mammals evolved, over the millions of years, into creatures with some capacity for thought, brain power beyond that of any of their ancestors. And that, to me, is the distinction of the mammal, not the biological fact that the mammal bears its young alive and nurtures them with its own milk.

Mammals have been evolving ever since Triassic times, more than 150 million years ago. The mammalian brain has been growing all that time, in one direction or another, and the vagaries of nature and environment have somewhat shaped that brain's capacities. Why and exactly how man evolved is still a mystery, but here he is, endowed with the best brain of all, the biggest capacity for reason and, as far as we know, the most active memory and imagination. It is a long way back to the giant lizards and the lesser variants from which the first tentative mammals must have evolved, but out of that variant in life form came the world we know today. You and I are a result of all those millennia of change, and I refuse to admit that the decisive factor was either an opposed thumb or the ability to walk erect on two legs.

The factors of evolution are many and complex, but it seems unlikely that the course of life ever took a more decisive turn than the one which began enlarging a primitive nerve center into a brain, which began displacing instinct with the fundamental power of reason. It was at that point that man began his course here on earth, when some mysterious variant in the genes prompted the first glimmering of thought.

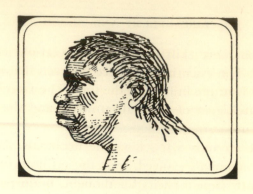

Man

Most Mysterious Mammal

Iᴛ ɪs ironic but true that man, the tireless questioner and investigator, knows almost all there is to know about the ancestry and evolution of the horse but does not know how or when or even where man himself originated as a species. Man remains a mystery to man, though there are theories and speculations and probabilities, and there is a limited amount of recognizable evidence of man's origins.

It seems certain that man is not a direct descendant of the apes. It seems equally certain that man and ape had a common ancestor somewhere back down the dim corridor of time, but no one has yet discovered that ancestor. Evolutionists believe that the common ancestor was an insect-eating, forest-dwelling creature something like the lemurs of today. In such animals, they believe, were acute senses, a high degree of potential intelligence, and higher-than-average manual dexterity. Eventually, according to this theory, these pre-men learned to walk on two legs and developed intelligence and reasoning power that in some degree substituted for the age-old animal habit of living solely by instinct.

The time scale for such a process of evolution is too vague to specify, but those who hold this theory come down eventually to the Tertiary period, perhaps forty million years ago, and base their further reasoning on geographic and climatic change.

They start the next phase of this reasoning with the geologic fact that major topographical changes occurred, particularly in central Asia, at about this time, in the Tertiary period. Mountains were thrust higher than ever before, particularly the Himalayas. North of the Himalayas the climate changed from warm and humid to cold and dry. South of the mountains the warm, wet climate continued much as before. Before this vast geologic change the whole area had been one huge semitropical forest. After the change the trees vanished north of the mountains, but the forests persisted south of the mountains.

Throughout this whole area, according to this reasoning, there had been a thriving population of the lemuroid animals. When the Himalayas rose to the dimensions of a forbidding barrier, those animals were divided into two groups. Those to the south of the mountains continued their forest life and eventually evolved into apes. Those north of the mountains, caught in a dry, cold, inhospitable region without trees, were forced either to adapt to the rigorous new conditions or to perish. They adapted and became the ancestors of man.

Thus goes the theory. It is based in part on the well-supported belief that difficult living conditions bring out the best of the potentialities in any given species. Obviously, only the fittest survive. In this instance, the ones most fit to survive would have been those with the highest intelligence and the greatest adaptive capacity. Without the readily available food supply of a

223

lush woodland, they broadened their diet and became omnivorous. The search for food on a vast, cold, grassy plain forced them to become nomads, traveling from one source of food to another. Difficult living conditions sharpened their wits and put a premium on intelligence. The dull-witted ones died young and did not perpetuate themselves. The strong, clever, intelligent ones survived to pass along their superior qualities to their offspring. With plant food scarce they became meat eaters and hunters. The hunt eventually demanded weapons. The cold demanded some form of clothing. They learned primitive craftsmanship. Without trees there was no place to hide from their enemies, so they learned the value of common defense. Communal life, the tribe, came into being. Because they were mammals and their young matured slowly, family life was imposed upon them. That led to the training of the immature, and that in turn fostered intelligence.

So much for this theory, which has a degree of plausibility even though the evidence to support it is largely circumstantial. But it seems undeniable that some such species did appear and survive, that it did increase in intelligence and manual dexterity, and that it eventually evolved speech. Speech meant communication beyond the level of grunts and squeals. With speech the primitive two-legged animal, wherever it came from and when, had the medium for exchange of ideas and experience. It became a man. The earliest evidence of primitive man yet found gives clear evidence of brain capacity sufficient for intelligent speech.

Anthropologists are wary of specific dates in relation to the very earliest man, but until recently the earliest fossil evidence of recognizable man was conceded to be about one million years old. In 1958 the skeleton of a manlike creature called Oreopithecus (a word meaning mountain ape), which anthropologists believe to have lived ten to twelve million years ago, was discovered near Grosseto, Italy. Significantly, scientists speak of it as manlike, not even as a primitive specimen of man, and initially regarded it as proof that man began differentiating from the remote man-ape ancestor long before the time previously accepted. This discovery may, in time, push the horizon back much further than it has yet been believed to be; but at the time I write the earliest date for identifiable man remains about one million years ago.

The problem of dating is indicated by the fact that for years it was believed that there was only one ice age during the Quaternary period, and that man dated from that ice age. Now it is known that there were at least four ice ages during that period. With each discovery of another authenticated ice age, man's history has been pushed back a few more thousand years. The dating probably will be revised again. The discovery of Oreopithecus may push it back by still more thousands of years.

Acceptance of even this antiquity is relatively new. As recently as a century ago many were saying that, on the evidence in the Bible, man's total history could not be much more than six thousand years. This seems absurd today, but it was not until the latter half of the nineteenth century that our scientists and investigators began delving deeply into the remote past and accepting the idea that man was a much older creature than had been generally supposed. Significantly, Biblical scholars as well as geologists and anthropologists had a hand in this revolution in thinking. For instance, they found that much of the time sequence in the Old Testament was symbolic rather than literal, and that some of the classic stories such as the account of the Flood were much older than the people who set them down in the Bible. Archaeologists and Biblical scholars, working together in the Near East, pushed back the story of mankind many, many centuries.

Meanwhile the geologists and anthropologists elsewhere were gathering data that pointed undeniably toward primitive man who lived and groped toward civilization many thousands of years ago. By early in the present century the rough outlines of the picture of early man had begun to take shape, though the dates given for his emergence as a species were still inconclusive. Only in the past fifty years have the dates been pushed back as far as one million years.

There are two principal types of evidence of primitive man's existence. One is skeletal remains, all of which are fossilized. Skeletal remains of those remote days, at least as far as man is involved, are exceedingly rare. Primitive man seems seldom to have chosen as his deathbed a place where his bones would be readily preserved. For that matter, few fossil remains of primitive apes have been found either. Apparently the apes, too, had the wit to avoid quicksands, tar pits and other fossil factories.

The other type of evidence is the cultural record: tools, weapons, ornaments, anything that clearly shows man's handiwork. In some instances, charcoal from fire is regarded as evidence, particularly if it is found in association with man-made tools or other artifacts.

Until recently, both types of evidence have been relatively difficult to date. This difficulty is now being overcome with such new techniques as the radioactive-carbon tests and the atomic-disintegration tests, but until they were discovered the only means of dating bones or artifacts was in geological terms. If a skeletal fragment or a chipped stone implement was found in a known stratum of rock, the geologists could say approximately how old the rock was and thus the bone or tool was dated. The geologists have their own tables by which to date the various strata in most areas of the earth. Trouble arose, of course, when bones or artifacts were found in a geological formation that had been much disturbed by convulsion of the earth's crust. Violent earthquake or volcanic action can jumble the geological evidence.

The most reliable human evidence thus far discovered has come primarily from river valley deposits and limestone caves.

River valley deposits can be dated with considerable accuracy, and the age of a limestone cave is written in the stone itself.

The oldest skeletal remains yet found that can be classed as possibly human, not prehuman, were in Java and China. Java Man, Pithecanthropus Erectus, was discovered by a Dutch surgeon near Trinil, Java, in 1889. Several skull portions, jaws, teeth and other fossil bones have been found, enough for the anthropologists to determine that Java Man had a brain somewhat below the capacity of modern man but well above that of all known apes. Java Man has been dated at close to one million years old, early in the Pleistocene period. No tools or implements have been found associated with Java Man's fragmental bones.

Just before World War I the first skeletal remains of Peking Man were found near Chicken Bone Hill in northern China. Subsequently, parts of more than thirty-five examples of Peking Man were found in the same area, as well as chipped stone implements and evidence that he used fire. Peking Man's intelligence apparently was about the same as that of Java Man, and the two have been dated as belonging to approximately the same period. The Peking Man fossils and their associated implements are considered one of the most notable of all discoveries of very ancient man.

Until recently it was believed that the oldest human evidence in Europe was the Piltdown Man, identified from skeletal parts presumably discovered in Sussex, England, and dated about 250,000 years later than Java Man. Investigation now seems to discredit the authenticity of Piltdown Man, at least of the fossils that for years have been accepted as proof of his existence. Elsewhere in England, however, flint implements tentatively dated as about the same age as the discredited Piltdown Man have been discovered, and there are evidences of human use of fire that seem to date from about the same time. No skeletal remains have been found in association with these fragments of evidence.

The next authenticated remains, which seem to date from the pause between the third and fourth advances of the Pleistocene glaciers and may be about 250,000 years old, are represented by the Heidelberg Man. His jawbone, but no other recognizable part, was found in glacial deposits near Heidelberg, Germany. Anthropologists relate Heidelberg Man to Neanderthal Man, discovered in 1856 in a cave in the gorge of the Neanderthal River near Düsseldorf, Germany.

It is worth noting that a considerable assortment of stone implements believed to be about the same age as Heidelberg Man has been found in eastern England. They are credited to members of the Heidelberg group, who could easily have traveled back and forth between present England and the Continent because the North Sea had not yet been formed and England was a peninsula, not yet an island.

Neanderthal Man has become the prototype for a whole race that ranged Europe, Africa and Asia during the early and middle Pleistocene times. Neanderthal Man had a low, sloping forehead, prominent eyebrow ridges, and a broad, flattened skull. His brain size was somewhat larger than that of the average modern European. He was of short, stocky stature, big-boned and powerful in build, and he had strong jaws and a retreating chin.

Neanderthal Man left remains in many places throughout Europe. Besides skeletal remains, quarries have been found, and camp sites with an extensive assortment of chipped stone implements. Neanderthal Man clearly evolved a rather full Early Stone Age culture.

Some anthropologists believe that Neanderthal Man was the ancestor of later, more advanced races. Others believe that the Neanderthals were conquered and displaced by an invasion of more intelligent, more vigorous people who originated in the plateau region of central Asia. More rigorous living conditions, say these anthropologists, made the invaders a stronger, more intelligent race, and they prevailed. If that is what happened, it was in the pattern of subsequent human history, for the outlanders, the barbarians from a rigorous homeland, have repeatedly overrun and conquered native races that grew relatively soft and content in a more hospitable land.

Whatever happened, three different types of primitive men were in Europe during the later stages of the ice ages of the Pleistocene, all of them of the human species and all with somewhat higher intelligence than the early Neanderthals. Best known of them, and probably most advanced, were the Cro-Magnons, named for five skeletons discovered in 1868 at Cro-Magnon, France. Subsequently, Cro-Magnon remains were found in many parts of Europe.

The Cro-Magnons were larger in stature than the average modern European and had a slightly larger brain. Their heads were shaped somewhat like those of the modern Eskimo, the skull narrow and the cheekbones wide, with a strong jaw and a well-developed chin, the forehead high. In point of time, the Cro-Magnons overlapped the late Neanderthals. Quite possibly they had a hand in eliminating the Neanderthals, perhaps by war, perhaps by absorption and crossbreeding. Neanderthal bones, cracked for their marrow, have been found in what appeared to be a Cro-Magnon cave in present Jugoslavia. The inference is that someone with cannibalistic tastes helped eliminate the Neanderthals, and the finger seems to point at the Cro-Magnons.

The Cro-Magnons, cannibalistic or not, had a considerably higher type of culture than the Neanderthals. They left the remarkable examples of prehistoric art found in the caves of France and Spain. They made excellent tools and weapons from stone and bone, and they knew how to use the drill and the chisel. Some anthropologists believe that traces of original Cro-Magnon stock can still be found in ethnic pockets of southern France and Brittany, though it seems likely that the Cro-

Magnons declined as a race and subsequently vanished. One theory is that Europe was overrun and repopulated by an unknown people from Asia or Africa, who became the basic stock for modern Europeans. These later people, whoever they were, established the Neolithic, or New Stone Age, culture, with ground and polished stone implements and some form of primitive agriculture.

There are traces of two other primitive races which seem to have influenced the types of certain modern Europeans and which lived in Europe, and probably elsewhere, at about the same time as the Cro-Magnons. One, the Chancelade, named for Chancelade in western France, where the first skeletal remains were found, was of short stature and much like the present-day Eskimos. The other, the Grimaldi, was a Negroid type and probably came from Africa. The Grimaldi skeletal remains were found in a Cro-Magnon cave in Italy.

Prehistoric Americans thus far revealed have all been of the Mongoloid type. Presumably they migrated here from Asia when there was a land bridge across Bering Strait. Their date of arrival here has been estimated at somewhere between thirty and fifty thousand years ago. Few really ancient skeletal remains have been found, but cultural evidence, particularly chipped flint tools and weapons, has been plentiful. The date is comparatively late in man's development as a species, and it is not now expected that Neanderthal Man's remains will be discovered on this continent. Nor Cro-Magnon Man, for that matter. The earliest Americans in all probability had their racial beginnings elsewhere.

The Central American culture of the Mayas, one of two higher prehistoric cultures in America, was of a still more recent date, well within the span of historic Europe. The Mayans, however, were of the same stock as the less developed Indians of North America. And Mayan culture, which included astronomy and mathematics, was independently evolved, with no assistance from the Old World. That culture, with the parallel Aztec culture of Mexico, evolved late in mankind's history, but it is eloquent testimony to the human capacity for intellectual growth and achievement, for it evolved in a primitive people who migrated into an area that was a cultural vacuum. We still do not know what ended the Mayan culture, but we know that the Aztec culture was still flourishing when the first Europeans arrived. We shall never know what heights it might have achieved under its own impetus, for the arrival of the conquistadors in the sixteenth century put a violent end to it. And soon after the conquest of Mexico the Mayan remnants of glory were brought down by the invaders.

This whole span of human evolution is full of gaps and missing chapters. There are peculiar mysteries along the way, and there are traps even for the wary. For example, it was believed not long ago that a race of human or prehuman giants lived in southeastern Asia about a million years ago and either perished as natural misfits or were killed by medium-sized primitive men who considered them freakish rivals. The source of this speculation was a few skeletal fragments found in southern China and Java—a massive jaw and a few huge teeth. The theory seemed to be supported by the fact that giantism was not uncommon among animals in the time and place indicated by the skeletal fragments. But no evidence of either tools or fire was found, and further examination of the evidence persuaded paleontologists that the bones were those of huge apes, not of either man or pre-man. So the theory of the giant men of Asia was discredited.

On the other hand there were the fire apes, as some call them. Science knows them as Australopithecus prometheus, a misleading name to the layman since their skeletal remains were found in South Africa, not Australia. These fire apes were pygmies, about four feet tall, and their brains were less than half the size of modern man's brain. When their fossil bones were first found, not many years ago, they were described as rather advanced types of apes. But further search revealed that these "apes" had used tools and possessed fire. They were not men, perhaps, in the sense that Java Man was a man, for they seemed to lack the capacity for full human intelligence. And yet they could not have been missing-link ancestors of the man race either, since their remains dated back only to a time when recognizable man was already in existence. But there they were, apelike creatures that used tools and at least experimented with fire. They, too, vanished, and one theory suggests that the kind of primitive men we recognize as our own ancestors killed them off because they were potential rivals, because they used tools and had begun to master fire, man's distinctive possession.

The same theory that had to be discarded in the instance of the giant creatures of Asia seems to be valid, thus far at least, in the instance of the fire-ape pygmies of Africa. The distinction turns not only on classification of fossil bones, but on a chipped flint tool and a handful of ancient charcoal. Man's identification rests, at least in part, not only on what kind of creature he was in skeletal terms, but on what he did with a piece of flint and a spark of fire.

One wonders why and how man evolved at all. Not why in a spiritual sense, but in a physical and intellectual sense. One wonders about the factors that dictated lines and directions of evolution, and one looks at the time span and is even more puzzled. At the very most, man has been here in recognizable form no more than a million and a half years, according to present knowledge. That is but a small fraction of time in the big terms. Life of some kind presumably has been here on earth a thousand times that long. Were 1,350 million years spent in preparing for the evolution of man? Arrogant as man is, that does seem somewhat too much to believe.

Over the long millennia there were countless upheavals of land, changes of climate, and alterations of living conditions.

Is one to believe that the convulsion which lofted the Himalayas, or some other mountain chain, perhaps, was the only event that created precisely the right conditions to compel one particular kind of animal to sharpen its wits, vary its diet, double its brain capacity and become a two-legged creature that could learn to talk and tame fire? It seems incredible.

Yet down the long corridors of time at least half a dozen incredible events occurred, as we now read the evidence. Life appeared. That was the first one, and we still have to take that on faith and the evidence of life all around us today. Then several single-celled bits of life came together and became a living unit of primitive complexity. That was the second incredible event. From that first form of complex life evolved a fish. That was the third miracle. A fish left the water and became an amphibian and the amphibian became a land-dwelling reptile with lungs. That was the fourth one. Somewhere along the way some larval form of sea life crept ashore, breathed air and became an insect. That was the fifth miraculous happening. And a reptile became a bird and another reptile became a mammal, with a brain that had the latent power of thought and reason.

If I accept these incredible events—and I must, in the light of present knowledge—then I must accept the most incredible one of all, the rise of man, the existence of myself and all my own sentient, searching kind.

I can accept it, but the whys persist; and the evolutionists' theories and their facts can explain but they cannot answer. Each time one of these incredible changes occurred, I am told, there was a waiting gap in the spectrum of life, a place for the new creation. But was the gap really there, or did the new type of life create the gap by its own vigorous pressure? Did man evolve because there was a waiting place for him, or did he create that place by his own cunning and ruthlessness?

Change, I am told, is the one certainty of life; change and adaptation have been continuous. I can accept that. But why, if change is inevitable, does the simplest form of life, the form that presumably was among the earliest in existence on this earth, still persist? And if there is a ruthless weeding out of the weak and unfit, why did the insignificant primitive mammals not perish through the 150 million years of lizard supremacy? Why did man, a physical weakling even among the mammals, survive long enough to perfect a brain and his own dominant intelligence?

The persistent whys! But, significantly, it is man himself, not the amoeba or the fish or the lizard or the bird, who asks the questions. And that, ultimately, is the mark of man—the search, the need to know, to understand.

The Enduring Pattern

I OPENED a fresh comb of honey this morning and as I sliced into it I thought that while any drafting student could draw more accurate hexagons there wasn't a draftsman or chemist alive who could secrete the wax, build the comb, and fill it with honey of his own manufacture. That comb and every drop of honey in it were made by insects that have virtually no intelligence but only a complexity of instincts. To make this one-pound comb of honey the bees had to visit about two million flowers and collect nectar from them. Then I remembered the insect-rich fossil beds at Florissant, Colorado, which prove that bees such as those we know today were here on earth and un-doubtedly making honey in hexagonal combs during the Tertiary period, about sixty million years ago. Bees and nectar and honey are no new phenomenon.

If life had no more than a mathematically accidental beginning, and if it essentially is no more than a chance, fortuitous combination of chemical elements in a special order, how did such different but intimately related living things as a bee and a nectar-yielding blossom come into being? Why did the blossom, with no vital need for the plant's excess sugar, which is nectar, develop a means for secreting it to lure a bee which will assist in the pollination of that particular flower? And how did the bee learn that this nectar could be made into concentrated, high-energy food, honey? How did the bee learn to gather nectar, convert it into honey, and store it in just this way?

A host of other questions might be asked about this particular matter, but they all lead toward more fundamental ideas, toward the very basis of life, why it evolved as it did and what is its meaning.

Life has its own urgencies, even the mutual urgencies of the bee and the blossom. And we are told that change is a law of nature. I see evidence of this all around me, though I note that there are exceptions. But even if I grant that law of change, I must ask where that law originated. In nature, I am told, in the nature of things as they are. Very well, but if change is a law of nature and inevitable, then the law of change must itself be some kind of exception. There can be no immutable laws unless something beyond nature, beyond the whole scope of our knowledge of changing nature, established those laws.

Science deals with facts, and the largest fact of which I am aware is the universe. Of that universe, the only portion I can even hope to know intimately is the earth. I am of that earth, a member of its vast community of living things. All around me are evidences of the earth and the life upon it. Facts.

To the best of my knowledge, bolstered by the knowledge of ten thousand other questioners and investigators, life first appeared here on this earth in the simplest single-celled form we can know or imagine. From that simplest form, all the kinds of life I know have evolved. It required, according to the approximate timetable we now use, about one and a half billion years to reach the multitude of complex life forms of today, with man the most complex of all. That is the way we think of it, though there still are processes in nature that, for all our prodding and probing, we cannot explain. Often we can say how, or when, or where, but only occasionally can we say why.

Life changed. It evolved, presumably upward, at least toward the more complex. Those original single-celled flecks of life began congregating and specializing, so that multi-celled forms of life appeared. This, presumably, was in response to that law of change. Change, of course, could have been downward instead of upward, and it probably was in many instances. Instead of combining, some of those flecks of life must have disintegrated, destroyed their own living entity, turned back toward nonliving form. But there was another factor at work, and this one we cannot explain. That was the persistence of the simple, the uncomplex. The single-celled form of life did not vanish in the urgency to combine and become increasingly complex. It continued, and still persists, substantially as it must have been in the beginning. In other words, there was an exception to the law of change.

True, change did occur repeatedly and even magnificently. Multicelled creatures became fish with backbones. Multicelled plants became seaweed and rushes and horsetails. And, for some reason which we ascribe to climate, some of the fish left the water and some of the plants ventured onto dry land. Why did the first amphibians and the first land plants leave the water? Because, we say, life had evolved to a point where it could live in this new, open-air environment, and when land appeared above the waters it invited life. Nature, we say, tends to populate the vacant environment.

But life seems to have been successful, even to the point of continuous evolutionary change, in the old environment, the water. Why should this venture away from the water have been made at all? It was full of chance and danger, and from all the evidence we have it was made by both plants and animals that were not yet ready to make the change completely. They kept returning to the water, the animals to lay their eggs, the plants simply to survive. And, again, most of the original water-dwelling examples of life persisted where they were. Was change really essential, particularly such violent and demanding change as from water to land?

At about this time, in the very dim past, the first of the primitive insects appeared, insects and spiders and scorpions. One widely accepted theory is that they evolved from larval forms of sea life. How they evolved is a persistent mystery. Some believe that they first ventured onto land to escape enemies in the water. But the forms of sea life from which they are supposed to have evolved remained in the water and persisted, despite those enemies. Yet here came the spiders and the insects, to achieve a perfection of form and a way of life that have continued with little change for perhaps 100 million years. Even if I grant the urgency of change at the beginning, at the time of their emergence, how shall I explain the relative lack of change after they had achieved a successful way of life in this new environment, the open air? What happened to that law of change?

Life originally, as far as we know, reproduced by a simple process of self-division. That method is still in use among a vast number of simple life forms, essentially unchanged from the process that was in use a billion years ago. But along the way the spore-bearing plants evolved, and the spore-bearers became flowering plants, with seeds. And along the way the animals began to lay eggs, each egg a minute fraction of one parent; and those eggs required fertilization with sperm, minute fractions of the other parent. Sex entered the picture.

Was this, too, an example of the law of change in action? If that were so, why did the spore-bearers persist among the plants, and why do primitive animals survive and continue to lay primitive eggs? From the naked, water-borne egg to the fetal, mammal-borne child is a long step, but no longer than from the spore of the fern to the multikerneled ear of Indian corn. The spore has an essential simplicity about it, wasteful as it may be as a reproductive means, and the kernel of corn on a maize plant is infinitely complex, the result of an involved and elaborate process. And the mammalian method of reproduction is a slow, involved process that produces immature offspring with a long and dangerous childhood.

Is complexity an end in itself, or is it merely a result of persistent and immutable change?

As I understand it, this rule of change tends toward improvement, toward perfection. There are contrary examples, where reversions have occurred, but they seem to be relatively rare. Perfection implies a purpose, and I suppose one might state that purpose, in life terms, is the ideal adaptation to environment. And since the environment persists in changing, then the purpose itself, or at least the ideal adaptation, must change with it. But is environment the only governing factor?

There have been a number of major steps in this process of change, steps which were outstanding landmarks in the history of life. Some of them may have been dictated by changes in environment, but others seem to have had no such cause. Indeed, some appear to have preceded environmental changes. And for these major steps man has only the sketchiest of explanations.

The single cell grouped with its neighbors and became a complex organism, a single community of related cells.

The primitive fish became amphibians and learned to live a part of their lives on land.

The reptiles laid eggs which had been fertilized in the female and which had their own protective coverings and contained food for the hatching young.

The mammals hatched their eggs inside their own bodies and gave birth to live young.

Primitive nodes of cranial nerves, which served primarily to transmit instinctive orders, grew into brains of varying complexity and capacity.

Man appeared, a physically weak animal endowed with more brain power than any creature that preceded him. He learned to remember, to reason, to think, to talk.

Why did these epochal things happen? They were far beyond the probability of even persistent change and adaptive evolution, beyond the probable response to changing environment. Yet they did happen, and in several instances they appear to have happened with almost explosive speed and impact on the life around them.

Groping for answers, we sometimes come up with mutations. There are variations within every species, we point out, a result of genes which for some reason rearrange themselves and create altered patterns. We do not know why mutations occur. We do know that some mutations die out, and that mutations which are better fitted to survive than the offspring which closely follow the parental pattern survive and multiply. Thus, we say, originated the various species. And if we are baffled by the vast differences between the bee and the bear, the mole and the elephant, the spider and the mockingbird, we are reminded that life has been changing for many millions of years and that there must have been many mutations and a long process of evolution.

Why have we so little evidence of transition forms? Such forms in the process of change, we are reminded, must have been rare until the direction of change was well established. That is why our fossil evidence gives us only a cross section of relatively stable life forms.

It all sounds plausible. That is the way it could have happened. But did it happen that way? Were there no other forces at work?

Man's arrogance with his "explanations" is matched only by the magnitude of his errors. Only a century ago many men were saying, with self-assured certainty, that the earth was created about 4000 B.C. Only a century ago the idea of evolution was a fugitive thought, counter to most knowledge and belief. Darwin and Wallace did not propound their evolutionary theories in a vacuum, but scientific knowledge was so limited that those theories created intellectual turmoil. Fifty years ago it was believed that the atom was the ultimate particle of matter. Now we have found thirty or more elements of matter or energy in the atom and describe it as a kind of submicroscopic universe. We have found that light, heat, energy, matter itself, are so closely interrelated that we seek a master mathematical formula to encompass them all.

We have propounded "laws" which govern the phenomena of matter and energy. But no one has yet found the source of those "laws," those patterns of form and action.

We have come a long way in piecing together our scraps of information and our fragmentary knowledge of life and time and matter. We may be on the trail of ultimate truth. On the other hand, we may be only rationalizing our knowledge to this point and blinding ourselves to something beyond. Our scientists may yet synthesize a chromosome or a gene, but will they even then have discovered the source or meaning of life?

Life is an amazing thing, but we have allowed some phases of our scientific thinking to obscure the wonder of it. The purpose of science is to know, but periodically man becomes so persistent in his search for documented knowledge that he mistakes the documentation for the knowledge itself. Repeatedly man has so engulfed himself in facts that he has lost sight of their meaning. Facts are tools, not an end in themselves, tools for the shaping of understanding. Perhaps the most remarkable fact about life is that man both participates in it and tries to explain and understand it. He sometimes loses sight of the fact that he himself is a part of the life that he is so assiduously investigating. And he does not always remember that life is itself a fact.

There must be a pattern in life. There is no other way to explain it satisfactorily. All the evidence we have points directly away from the chaos of pure chance and toward order of some kind. Man himself is the best evidence we have close at hand; and although man himself is the investigator it seems undeniable that the pattern has dictated life as we know and experience it. Perhaps change is inevitable, but not random change. The whole order of life, from the single-celled form down to man himself, denies that possibility.

If there is a law of change, then there must be some pattern to the change. I will accept the belief that certain external factors somewhat dictate the manner of that change. On the evidence at hand, I cannot deny this. But behind that law of change there must be a force of change, a life force of some kind. Call it urgency, call it persistence, call it what you will, it must be there, somewhere.

Those who explain the origin of life as a chance combination of chemical elements which they admit could not happen under the conditions of today are falling back, perhaps unconsciously, on some force that brought about that chance combination. What was it? Those who believe that life appeared in the primordial seas from some remote place in outer space are admitting the existence of life elsewhere at that time. Where and how did *that* life come into being? Those who trace the germ of life to nucleic acid and say the substance of the genes can be duplicated, admit that they do not know whence the genes, or the nucleic acid, received their power of life or the patterns they dictate. Where lies that power, that pattern? If it is in the way those elusive elements combine, why do they combine that way?

The questions are persistent and most difficult. They are posed by everything around me—the bee in the hive, the clover blossom at the roadside, the honey on my breakfast table, a man asking questions. Perhaps we shall never know the answers. Perhaps man, at his present stage, cannot accept an answer that does not conform to chemical formulas or mathematical equations. Or perhaps the formulas and equations will eventually lead to the simplicity of a pattern, a force, a rhythm, that is really ultimate and we shall be forced to accept a fact, a documentation, without the ultimate meaning. If so, that force, that pattern or purpose, will persist despite the equation. And some men will call it reason, and some will call it God, as man has done for thousands of years. The naming will not too much matter. The recognition will be of overwhelming importance.

Meanwhile, here am I, and here are millions of other human beings, on a habitable earth which we now believe has been spinning about the sun for thousands of millions of years. Our astrophysicists, seeking facts and probabilities, tell us that it will continue to spin in such a habitable orbit, such a pattern, for perhaps another 5,000 million years. And to the best of our knowledge, man as a species has been here only about one million years.

Here am I, in one small valley on this earth, with the necessities of life and human comfort available to me, and endowed with the means of reason and thought. By my own judgment, I am among the most fortunate of the earth's creatures. Around me are not only the works of man, my own kind, but the vastly more enduring creations of nature. I have not the simplicity of the newt or the fiercely efficient society of the ants and the bees, and I have not the quiet patience of the maple tree or the age-old economy of the algae that live and proliferate in the stagnant water of the bogland just down the road. I am a complex organism, subject to worry and pain and disappointment, but also capable of joy and satisfaction.

Who am I? I am the latest, but probably not the last, in a long, unbelievably long, line of changing life. I know that far more simple forms of life have persisted much longer than my own kind. I know that there are forms of life that are, in terms of efficiency in living, far more successful than mankind has yet proved itself to be. But I have no knowledge of any other living thing that can live as variously and can think and feel and create as successfully as I can.

Where am I? I am in one small valley on one relatively insignificant mass of land on a minor planet in the solar system. That planet circling about the sun receives light and warmth from that sun which makes the kind of life I know possible. This solar system is one of many in a universe of which I am aware, for the most part, only on cloudless nights, a universe vastly larger than I can readily comprehend. This planet, this solar system, this universe as far as I can know it, is a part of a pattern that remains complex beyond my understanding, for all the knowledge that my own kind have amassed. But this planet itself is proof, to me, of such a pattern, such a system of order and meaning.

What time is it? I can discover no absolutes in time. Time is all relative, whether I speak of a year or a microsecond, of a million years or of today. Time, for me, is comprehensible in terms of my own lifetime and its relationship to this earth. Time, in one sense, is experience, and in another sense time is duration. Science gives me approximate timetables for the earth, the solar system, the evolution of life, the disintegration of the atom. But to man, the sentient, questioning creature, time has simpler dimensions. It is only with difficulty that we can look back beyond yesterday or last year into the million years or more that we are told man has been here as man. And when we are asked to envision five billion more years on a habitable earth, we stand in awe at the incomprehensible. Both those assumptions in terms of time have vast importance, I am sure; but they still remain somewhere out in the haze of intangible time to a creature tied to a twenty-four-hour day and a 365-day year.

What time is it? It is now, today. It is that stage of man's development and man's self-education in living with his own kind and all kinds of life upon this earth. In that sense, it is not much after dawn. The day still lies ahead, for man at least. On that I can rest, believing that life does have meaning, that life does have pattern, that life is worth whatever span of time is mine or any man's to know, to feel, to think, to learn, to participate in this amazing thing, life itself.

About the Author

HAL BORLAND *was born in Nebraska, grew up in Colorado, has worked and traveled all over the United States, and for the past fifteen years has lived in rural Connecticut. He has written on many topics for newspapers and magazines here and abroad, but his continuing interest has been in man and his environment. He is an outdoor columnist for the* Berkshire Eagle *in Pittsfield, Massachusetts, and for the past sixteen years has written the weekly outdoor editorial essay for* The New York Times *Sunday editorial page. This is his fourteenth book. His previous books have included novels, poetry, essays, a book about the craft of writing and an autobiographical story of his Colorado boyhood. He also has collaborated on fiction with his wife, Barbara Dodge Borland. The Borlands live on their hill-and-valley farm in the lower Berkshire hills.*